Skills Practice
Workbook

**Level 2
Book 2**

Mc Graw Hill **SRA**

Columbus, OH

SRAonline.com

 SRA

Send all inquiries to this address:
SRA/McGraw-Hill
4400 Easton Commons
Columbus, OH 43219-6188

ISBN: 978-0-07-619472-8
MHID: 0-07-619472-8

8 9 10 11 12 13 QVS 20 19 18 17 16

The *McGraw-Hill* Companies

Table of Contents

Unit 4 Look Again

Unit 5 Courage

Unit 6 America's People

/o͞o/ spelled oo

Focus The /o͞o/ sound can be spelled *oo*.

Practice **Read the sentence. Change the word in the box to make a new rhyming word. Write the new word on the line.**

1. | **broom** | The bride and _____ had a fancy wedding.

2. | **moon** | We usually eat our lunch at _____.

3. | **noodle** | Aunt Jenny bought a _____ from the pet store.

4. | **pool** | The soup needs to _____ before we eat it.

5. | **mood** | Pepperoni pizza is Henry's favorite _____.

6. | **boots** | A plant has _____ that hold it in the ground.

7. | **gloom** | Many flowers _____ in the spring.

8. | **poof** | I heard the raindrops hitting the _____ during the thunderstorm.

 **Pick a word from the box below to complete each sentence. Write the word on the line.**

moon	scoop	bedroom	loose	boots
cartoons	zoomed	tools	pool	too

9. I can see the stars from my _____ window.

10. A mechanic uses _____ to repair cars.

11. On Saturday mornings I enjoy watching _____ on television.

12. The rocket _____ straight up into the sky.

13. My dentist said I have a tooth that is _____.

14. Tonya ate a small _____ of mashed potatoes with her dinner.

15. The cowboy had a spur on each of his _____.

16. Swimming in the _____ on a hot day feels great.

17. Alex wants to join us and play checkers _____.

18. Light from the _____ can help you see on a dark night.

Plurals

Focus
- Adding -s or -es to a word makes it plural.
- Plural words show that there is more than one.

Practice **Add -s or -es to each word to make it plural. Then write the new word on the line.**

1. book + s _____

2. trick + s _____

3. store + s _____

4. costume + s _____

5. marsh + es _____

6. glass + es _____

Apply **Add -s or -es to the word in parentheses ( ) to complete the sentence. Write the word on the line.**

7. I use the _____ on my paper to write neatly. (line)

8. Our baseball team has two _____. (coach)

9. Susan has four _____ on her bookbag. (patch)

10. Emily picked a bouquet of _____. (flower)

Synonyms and Antonyms

Focus

- Synonyms are words that are similar in meaning. *Tired* and *sleepy* are synonyms.
- Antonyms are words that are opposite in meaning. *Bad* and *good* are antonyms.

Practice Draw a line to match each word to its *synonym*.

1. choose   **a.** giggle

2. ill   **b.** select

3. laugh   **c.** angry

4. mad   **d.** sick

Draw a line to match each word to its *antonym*.

5. before   **a.** work

6. over   **b.** after

7. play   **c.** empty

8. full   **d.** under

Focus Selection Vocabulary

camouflage (kam' ə fläzh) *n.* A disguise that makes something look the same as the area around it. (page 20)

hidden (hid' ən) *adj.* Kept out of sight. (page 22)

mimicry (mim' i krē) *n.* The act of copying. (page 34)

patterns (pat' ərnz) *n.* Plural of **pattern:** the order of colors, shapes, or lines. (page 20)

surroundings (sə roun' dingz) *n.* The area around a person or thing. (page 24)

pretenders (prē tend' ûrz) *n.* Plural of **pretender:** something that makes believe it is something else. (page 34)

blend (blend) *v.* To mix together so as not to be seen. (page 24)

hunters (hun' tərz) *n.* Plural of **hunter:** an animal that chases other animals for the purpose of food. (page 23)

coat (kōt) *n.* The skin and fur of an animal. (page 24)

fooled (foold) *v.* Past tense of **fool:** to trick. (page 41)

Practice Write the word from the box that matches each definition below.

camouflage	hidden	surroundings	coat	patterns
pretenders	blend	hunters	mimicry	fooled

1. _____ to mix together so as not to be seen

2. _____ the skin and fur of an animal

3. _____ things that make believe they are something else

4. _____ kept out of sight

5. _____ a disguise that makes something look the same as the area around it

6. _____ tricked

7. _____ the act of copying

8. _____ animals that chase other animals for the purpose of food

9. _____ orders of colors, shapes, or lines

10. _____ the area around a person or thing

Name _____ **Date** _____

Selection Vocabulary

 **Apply** Write six sentences using at least one of the
vocabulary words in each sentence.

11. _____

_____

12. _____

_____

13. _____

_____

14. _____

_____

15. _____

_____

16. _____

_____

Fill in the blanks with vocabulary words to complete the following sentences. Then complete the activities.

17. _____ is a type of _____.

List an animal that copies. _____

18. Some animals have _____ that help

them _____ into their environment.

List two animals that use this type of camouflage.

_____

19. Some animals are good _____ , but

other animals need to stay _____ for protection.

Name an animal that would be good at making other animals

think it is something else. _____

20. Do not be _____ by friendly appearances. Some

animals are _____ that rely on other animals
for food.

Name two animals that chase other animals for the purpose

of food. _____

Selection Vocabulary • *Skills Practice 2*

Main Idea and Details

Focus
- The **main idea** tells what a paragraph is about. It is the most important idea presented by the author.
- **Details** provide more specific information about the **main idea**.

Practice
Look through "Animal Camouflage" for main idea sentences. Write a main idea sentence. Then give some details about the main idea.

Page: _____

Main idea sentence: _____

_____

_____

_____

Details about the main idea: _____

_____

_____

_____

_____

_____

Read the paragraph. It is missing a main idea sentence. Choose the best main idea sentence from the box, and write it on the lines. Then list details from the paragraph that support the main idea.

Sometimes animals are too small to defend themselves from harm. Camouflage is a useful tool to help keep them safe. The leaf insect and leafy sea dragon both look like the plants in their surroundings. Both animals even move like the leaves they mimic. Using a disguise keeps these animals alive.

Watching animals out in the wild is exciting.

It is fun to learn about animals.

Animals can use camouflage as protection from predators.

_____

_____

Details:

_____

_____

_____

_____

Charts

Look through "Animal Camouflage," and fill in the chart with information about the animals and how they use camouflage.

Animal Camouflage

	Who?	How?	Why?
1.			
2.			
3.			
4.			
5.			

Write the title of a chart you could make to help you with your unit investigation.

6. _____

_____

Think about the questions you want to investigate. Write your list of questions below.

7. _____

_____

8. _____

_____

9. _____

_____

10. _____

_____

Describing an Event

Think   **Audience: Who** will read your description?

_____

Purpose: What is your reason for writing a description?

_____

Prewriting   Use the web below to plan your description. Write the event you are describing in the center square. Then write descriptive details in the outer squares.

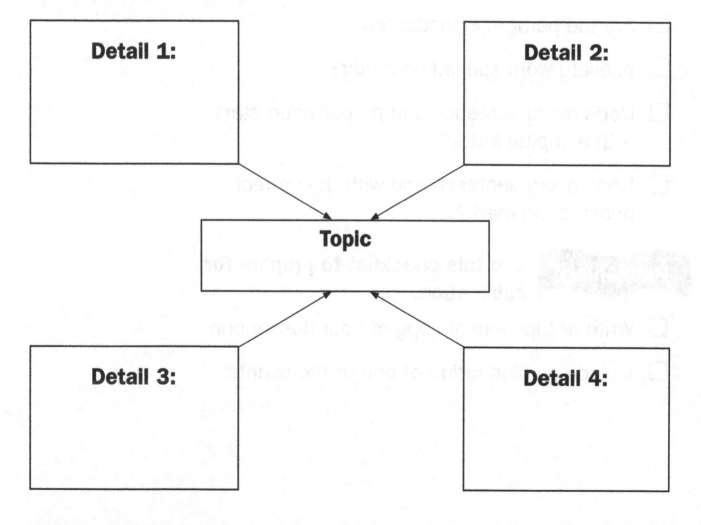

Detail 1:		Detail 2:
	Topic	
Detail 3:		Detail 4:

Revising — Use this checklist to revise.

☐ Are the events written in the correct order?

☐ Does every sentence support your topic?

☐ Is there any irrelevant information you need to delete?

☐ Did you use descriptive details?

☐ Were any details left out that you need to add?

Editing/Proofreading — Use this checklist to correct mistakes.

☐ Are the paragraphs indented?

☐ Is every word spelled correctly?

☐ Does every sentence and proper noun start with a capital letter?

☐ Does every sentence end with the correct punctuation mark?

Publishing — Use this checklist to prepare for publication.

☐ Write or type a neat copy of your description.

☐ Include an illustration of one of the events.

/o͞o/ spelled oo

Focus
- The /o͞o/ sound sounds like the underlined letters in the word m<u>oo</u>.
- One way the /o͞o/ sound can be spelled is oo.

Practice **Sort the spelling words under the correct heading.**

Write the spelling word that rhymes with the word *zoom:*

1. _____

2. _____

Write the spelling word that rhymes with the word *loop:*

3. _____

Write the spelling word that ends with the /o͞o/ sound:

4. _____

Write the remaining spelling words on the lines below:

5. _____   **8.** _____

6. _____   **9.** _____

7. _____   **10.** _____

Word List

1. hoop
2. tooth
3. mood
4. igloo
5. soon
6. bloom
7. food
8. room
9. pooch
10. pool

Challenge Words

11. noodle
12. rooster
13. school
14. bedroom
15. caboose

Proofreading Strategy Circle the misspelled spelling words. Write the words correctly on the lines below.

Spring is in full blume. Sune the birds will begin to look for fude to feed their babies, and the pul will open for the season. Spring really puts me in a good muud!

11. _____

12. _____

13. _____

14. _____

15. _____

Consonant-Substitution Strategy Replace the underlined letter or letters to create a spelling word.

16. _stoop_ + h = _____

17. _booth_ + t = _____

18. _gl_oom + r = _____

19. _sm_ooch + p = _____

20. _z_oo + igl = _____

Colons

Focus
- **Colons** are used to introduce a list.
- **Colons** also separate the hour and the minutes when writing the time.

Practice   **Place colons where they belong in the sentences below.**

1. At 2 10 the doors are locked.

2. We must leave the house by 1 30.

3. Her birthday party will begin at 5 00.

4. Lunchtime is at 12 15.

5. Place these things in your suitcase shoes, shorts, and shirts.

6. These are the best things in life love, music, and friends.

7. Your backpack should have these items paper, pencils, and folders.

8. Pack these items in your lunch sandwich, fruit, and drink.

Write colons where they have been left out in the paragraph below.

Ann's alarm woke her up at 7 30. She had to do many things to get ready shower, dress, and brush her teeth. It was 8 00 when she came downstairs to eat. For breakfast she had the usual eggs, toast, and milk. The bus arrived at 8 15 on the dot. Ann sat on the bus with her three best friends Margaret, Tonya, and Brittany. Her watch said it was 8 30 when she arrived at school. She was ready to start her day.

Write a sentence using the time or list in parentheses ( ). Write the time in numbers, and use colons and commas where they are needed.

9. (four-twenty) _____

_____

10. (pencils paper erasers) _____

_____

11. (nine-ten) _____

_____

12. (elephants zebras tigers) _____

_____

/o͞o/ spelled *u_e*, *_ew*, *_ue*, and *u*

Focus The /o͞o/ sound can be spelled with *u_e*, *_ew*, *_ue*, and *u*.

Practice Use the following words to fill in the blanks.

ruby	blew	truth	drew	rude
chew	tune	clue	flute	blue

Write the words with the /o͞o/ sound spelled like *grew*.

1. _____   3. _____

2. _____

Write the words with the /o͞o/ sound spelled like *June*.

4. _____   6. _____

5. _____

Write the words with the /o͞o/ sound spelled like *Sue*.

7. _____   8. _____

Write the words with the /o͞o/ sound spelled like *truly*.

9. _____   10. _____

Replace the underlined letter or letters to create a rhyming word. The new word will have the same spelling pattern for /o͞o/.

11. <u>c</u>lue + tr = _____

12. <u>d</u>ew + n = _____

13. <u>b</u>lue + g = _____

14. <u>pr</u>une + t = _____

Read the paragraph. Circle the misspelled words. Write the words correctly on the blanks below.

The Hare and the Tortoise is an old story. One day Tortoise and Hare argue over who is trewly the fastest runner. They decide to have a race to find out the truthe. Each animal just knue Hare would be the winner. Hare took a break and fell asleep by the bloo sprewce tree. Tortoise won the race by using the rewl of staying slow but steady.

15. _____

16. _____

17. _____

18. _____

19. _____

20. _____

Compound Words

> **Focus**
>
> A compound word is made when two words are put together to make a new word.
>
> **Example:**
>
> dog + house = doghouse

Practice   **Combine the words below to make a compound word. Write the compound word on the line.**

1. day + dream = _____

2. lady + bug = _____

3. tooth + brush = _____

4. gold + fish = _____

Apply   **Fill in each blank below with a compound word.**

5. A bath for a bird is a _____.

6. A cloth to put on the table is a _____.

7. A pot to put tea in is a _____.

8. A house for a doll is a _____.

Contractions

A contraction is a shortened form of a pair of words. An apostrophe (') is used to show where a letter or letters have been removed.

Example:
here + is = here's

Practice Read each sentence. Circle the pair of words that form the underlined *contraction.*

1. They're going to see the new giraffe at the zoo.
   a. They have   **b.** They are   **c.** They will   **d.** They did

2. Leslie and Steve wouldn't have a picnic in the rain.
   a. would it   **b.** would have   **c.** would not   **d.** would be

3. Mrs. Carter can't find her purple sweater.
   a. can not   **b.** can it   **c.** could not   **d.** could have

4. She's going to have a ballet lesson today.
   a. She will   **b.** She can   **c.** She did   **d.** She is

5. During art class we'll learn how to draw animals.
   a. we have   **b.** we did   **c.** we will   **d.** we should

6. I've been the classroom helper this week.
   a. I am   **b.** I have   **c.** I will   **d.** I was

Selection Vocabulary

Focus

meadow (med' ō) *n.* A field of grass. (page 52)

pond (pond) *n.* A small lake. (page 52)

scent (sent) *n.* A smell. (page 52)

disguise (dis gīz') *n.* Something that hides the way one looks. (page 59)

prying (prī ing) *v.* Looking at or into something too closely. (page 59)

slender (slen' dûr) *adj.* Thin. (page 58)

hare (hâr) *n.* A kind of rabbit. (page 50)

tender (ten' dûr) *adj.* Soft. (page 70)

stump (stump) *n.* The part of a tree that is left after the tree has been cut down. (page 56)

drowsy (drou' zē) *adj.* Sleepy. (page 64)

 **Fill in each blank with a word from the vocabulary list that completes the sentence.**

1. The _____ of toast filled the air in the kitchen.

2. I always feel _____ after lunch.

3. Tom fed the ducks that swam in the _____.

4. A small _____ jumped across the forest path.

5. The detective wore a _____ as he looked for clues.

6. My mother is tall and _____.

7. George saw a deer eating in the _____.

8. Is your steak _____?

9. Squirrels were using the wooden _____ to store nuts.

10. My aunt is known for _____ into other people's business.

Selection Vocabulary

Apply List an antonym and a synonym for the vocabulary words listed below.

Vocabulary Word	Synonyms	Antonyms
11. pond	_____	_____
12. tender	_____	_____
13. drowsy	_____	_____
14. prying	_____	_____
15. slender	_____	_____

Look at the following vocabulary words, and say them out loud. They should sound like words you have heard before. On the lines, write a different way to spell each word. Then provide definitions for both spellings.

_____ **hare**

_____   _____

_____

_____   _____ **scent**

_____

_____

Write a story about an animal that uses camouflage. Use all the vocabulary words in your story.

_____

_____

_____

_____

_____

_____

_____

_____

_____

_____

_____

_____

_____

_____

_____

_____

_____

_____

_____

_____

_____

_____

Making Observations

Record the animals you find on your field trip. Describe the place you found each animal. Then tell what the animal looked like. Did it blend into the area around it? Did it look like a tree, a limb, or a twig? Write your findings in the chart.

Animal	Where I found it	What it looked like

Pick two of the animals you found. Then tell why they were hard or easy to find.

1. _____

_____

_____

_____

2. _____

_____

_____

_____

Name _____ Date _____

Writing a Research Report

Audience: Who will read your research report?

_____

Purpose: What is your reason for writing a research report?

_____

Use the graphic organizer below to brainstorm topics for your research report.

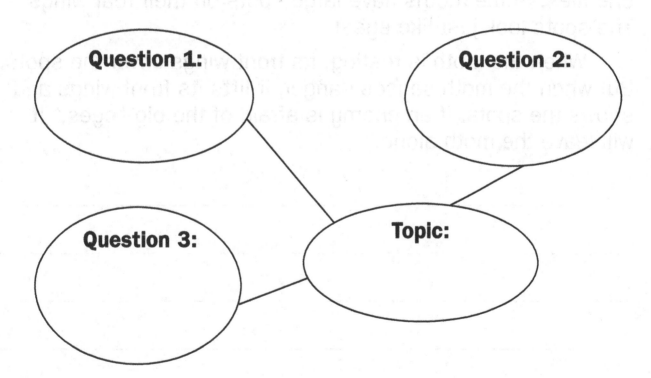

Question 1:

Question 2:

Question 3:

Topic:

Taking Notes

Practice **Use the lines below to take notes from the following paragraphs of "Animal Camouflage."**

Some animals have a shape or color that looks like something else. This type of camouflage is called mimicry. Animals that use mimicry are good pretenders.

The walkingstick is one insect that uses mimicry. Its long, thin, bumpy body looks just like a small branch!

Walkingsticks can even change color with the seasons. In the spring, the tree's branches and leaves are green. The walkingstick is green, too. When the branches and leaves turn brown, the walkingstick turns brown to match.

Some animals use other kinds of mimicry to fool their enemies. Some moths have large spots on their rear wings. The spots look just like eyes!

When the moth is resting, its front wings cover the spots. But when the moth senses danger, it lifts its front wings and shows the spots. If an enemy is afraid of the big "eyes," it will leave the moth alone.

_____

_____

_____

_____

_____

_____

/o͞o/ spelled *u, u_e, _ew, _ue*

Focus

- The /o͞o/ sound sounds like the word *new*.
- Some ways the /o͞o/ sound can be spelled are *u, u_e, _ew,* and *_ue.*

Practice **Sort the spelling words under the correct heading.**

/o͞o/ spelled *u:*

1. _____   2. _____

/o͞o/ spelled *u_e:*

3. _____   4. _____

/o͞o/ spelled *_ew:*

5. _____   7. _____

6. _____

/o͞o/ spelled *_ue:*

8. _____ 10. _____

9. _____

Word List

1. clue
2. blew
3. tube
4. June
5. student
6. dew
7. grew
8. due
9. ruby
10. overdue

Challenge Words

11. blueberry
12. salute
13. fluid
14. newsroom
15. assume

Meaning Strategy Write the spelling word next to its meaning clue.

11. small drops of water found in the morning _____

12. used air to move _____

13. time for something to be finished or turned in _____

14. past the time that something should
    be finished _____

Visualization Strategy Circle the correct spelling for each spelling word. Write the correct spelling on the line.

15. ruby   rooby   _____

16. clew   clue   _____

17. grew   grue   _____

18. Jewn   June   _____

19. tube   tueb   _____

20. student   stewdunt   _____

Contractions

Focus

• A **contraction** combines two words. In a contraction, some letters from one or both of the original words are left out, and an apostrophe (') takes the place of the missing letters.

Examples:

are not—aren't	do not—don't
I am—I'm	she is—she's
could have—could've	would have—would've

Practice **Circle the correct contraction in each sentence below.**

1. Greenland **isn't don't** a continent.

2. There **won't aren't** a lot of people living in Greenland.

3. Hawaii **wasn't weren't** a state until 1959.

4. I **won't haven't** be attending the event.

5. I **wouldn't haven't** heard any information on the test.

6. Tomorrow there **won't aren't** be a test.

7. **Don't isn't** worry about that.

8. It **won't would've** been nice to go on vacation.

 **Write the contraction for the boldfaced words in each sentence below.**

9. **I am** going to Arizona in April. _____

10. **I have** never been to the southwest states. _____

11. **I will** send you a postcard of the desert. _____

12. **She is** my best friend. _____

13. I know **he is** coming to visit today. _____

Add apostrophes where they are needed to make contractions. Use proofreading marks.

I couldnt think of anything to write. Were supposed to write a poem for class. It doesnt have to be a long poem. I cant think tonight! Couldnt I write about my life? I could, if it werent so late.

Write the contraction for the following words.

14. should not _____

15. he is _____

16. cannot _____

17. have not _____

18. there is _____

/oo/ spelled *oo*

Focus The /oo/ sound can be spelled with *oo*. The *oo* spelling pattern is usually found in the middle of a word.

Practice **Use the letters in parentheses ( ) to write a word on the line with the *oo* spelling pattern.**

1. (b, k) _____

2. (f, t) _____

3. (w, d) _____

4. (h, k) _____

5. (h, d) _____

6. (c, k) _____

7. (s, t, d) _____

8. (s, h, k) _____

9. (l, k) _____

10. (w, l) _____

Read each word, and then write a new rhyming word on the line.

11. book _____

12. hood _____

13. shook _____

14. look _____

15. stood _____

Complete each sentence by writing one of the above words on the blank line.

16. Our class is reading a _____ about animals and camouflage.

17. I put the _____ over my head when it started to rain.

18. Charlie _____ in line to ride the rollercoaster.

19. You have to _____ closely to see an octopus in hiding.

20. The earthquake _____ the ground.

Prefix *dis-*

Focus
- A prefix is added to the beginning of a word and changes the meaning of that word.
- The prefix *dis-* means "the opposite of" or "not."

Example:

dis + like = dislike (to not like)

Practice Add the prefix *dis-* to the base words below. Write the new word on the first line. Then write the meaning of the new word.

Base Word	New Word	New Meaning
1. obey	_____	_____
2. agree	_____	_____
3. trust	_____	_____
4. approve	_____	_____

Apply Write two sentences using the new words from above.

5. _____

6. _____

Focus

- A prefix is added to the beginning of a word and changes the meaning of that word.
- The prefix *un-* means "not."

Example:

    un + happy = unhappy (not happy)

Practice

Add the prefix *un-* to the base words below. Then write the meaning of each new word.

Base Word	New Word	New Meaning
1. locked	_____	_____
2. ripe	_____	_____
3. fair	_____	_____
4. stuck	_____	_____
5. kind	_____	_____

Apply

Fill in the blank with the prefix *dis-* or *un-* to create a new word that makes sense in the sentence.

6. Joe used a key to _____lock the door.

7. Mr. Collins does not like _____honesty.

8. It is _____usual for me to _____obey my parents.

Selection Vocabulary

Focus

delay (di lā') *v.* To take place at a later time. (page 87)

glides (glīdz) *v.* Moves in a smooth way. (page 85)

designed (di zīnd') *v.* Past tense of **design:** to plan or make. (page 94)

proceeds (prō sēdz') *v.* Moves on or continues. (page 97)

fade (fād) *v.* To lose color or brightness. (page 87)

drab (drab) *adj.* Plain and without color. (page 96)

grotesque (grō tesk') *adj.* Strange or ugly in shape or appearance. (page 88)

fail (fāl) *v.* To not succeed. (page 91)

creatures (krē' chərz) *n.* Plural of **creature:** a living thing. (page 82)

sporting (spôrt' ing) *v.* Wearing proudly. (page 87)

Draw a line from each word on the left to its definition on the right.

1. designed

a. living things

2. drab

b. to take place at a later time

3. fade

c. planned or made

4. grotesque

d. wearing proudly

5. creatures

e. moves in a smooth way

6. sporting

f. plain and without color

7. proceeds

g. to lose color or brightness

8. fail

h. to not succeed

9. glides

i. moves on or continues

10. delay

j. strange or ugly in shape or appearance

Name _____ **Date** _____

creatures	drab	designed	fade	grotesque
delay	glides	sporting	proceeds	fall

11. The hooks of a masked crab are _____ to hold seaweed onto its shell.

12. Many _____ use camouflage to stay safe.

13. An octopus _____ along the ocean floor.

14. If a cuttlefish is courting, he will be _____ stripes.

15. An enemy _____ by the sea dragon because it looks like seaweed.

16. Some sea creatures, such as the crab, are _____.

17. Stripes on a cuttlefish can _____, leaving it just one color.

18. Not all sea creatures are _____, but the sargassum fish can be described this way.

19. We had to _____ reading "How to Hide an Octopus and Other Sea Creatures" until we finished "Animals in Hiding."

20. Some sea creatures _____ to hide from their enemies.

21. glides *v.* _____

22. fail *v.* _____

23. grotesque *adj.* _____

24. proceeds *v.* _____

25. designed *v.* _____

26. sporting *v.* _____

27. fade *v.* _____

28. delay *v.* _____

29. creatures *n.* _____

30. drab *adj.* _____

Eliminating Irrelevant Information

Practice   Read the paragraph below. Eliminate any irrelevant information by writing a line through it.

Masked crabs are animals that use seaweed for protection. The crabs first tear the seaweed into pieces. Then they chew the seaweed until it is soft. Seaweed is a type of water plant. Then the crabs put the seaweed on their bodies.

Masked crabs live in the North Atlantic, North Sea, and Mediterranean Sea. The Mediterranean Sea is big. Masked crabs walks backward to burrow in the sand. The crabs use their antennae to make a breathing tube.

The crabs have reddish brown and yellow colors. Blue is my favorite color. The crabs normally are about four centimeters long. The males are twice as big as the females. The crabs have four teeth. Two of their teeth are between their eyes.

Masked crabs like to eat worms and mollusks. These creatures are found where it is sandy. You can find dead masked crabs on the beach.

Revising — Use this checklist to revise.

- ☐ Did you answer all your questions?
- ☐ Do you have one paragraph for each question?
- ☐ Did you use facts and special words correctly?
- ☐ Do your ideas and information flow smoothly?
- ☐ Is your report written in an interesting, lively way?

Editing/Proofreading — Use this checklist to correct mistakes.

- ☐ Is every word or special term spelled correctly?
- ☐ Did you capitalize the names of people and places?
- ☐ Does every sentence start with a capital letter?
- ☐ Does every sentence end with the correct punctuation mark?

Publishing — Use this checklist to prepare for publication.

- ☐ Write or type a neat copy of your report.
- ☐ Include a drawing, a photograph, or other visual aid with your report.
- ☐ Read your report to the whole class or to small groups of classmates.

/oo/ spelled oo

Focus The /oo/ sound is spelled oo, as in the word *cook*.

Practice **Sort the spelling words under the correct heading.**

Write the spelling words that rhyme with *cook*.

1. _____   3. _____

2. _____   4. _____

Write the spelling words that rhyme with *hood*.

5. _____   7. _____

6. _____

Write the spelling word that rhymes with *woof*.

8. _____

Write the other spelling words with the /oo/ sound.

9. _____   10. _____

Word List
1. look
2. good
3. soot
4. shook
5. stood
6. foot
7. brook
8. wood
9. hoof
10. hook

Challenge Words
11. uncooked
12. childhood
13. notebook
14. bookmark
15. understood

Pronunciation Strategy Choose the correct spelling for each word. Then pronounce each word carefully, and write it on the line below.

11. look   luk   _____

12. fute   foot   _____

13. stuud   stood   _____

14. hufe   hoof   _____

15. shook   shuk   _____

Consonant-Substitution Strategy Replace the underlined letter in each word with a new letter to form a spelling word.

16. <u>c</u>ook + h = _____

17. <u>h</u>ood + g = _____

18. <u>cr</u>ook + br = _____

19. <u>f</u>oot + s = _____

20. <u>st</u>ood + w = _____

Pronouns

Focus

A **pronoun** is a word that takes the place of a noun (person, place, or thing) in a sentence.

Singular Pronouns: *I, you, he, she, it, me, him, her*
Plural Pronouns: *we, they, them, us*

Rules:

- **Singular nouns** must be replaced with **singular pronouns.**

- **Plural nouns** must be replaced with **plural pronouns.**

- **Pronouns** must also match the **gender** of the nouns.

Examples:

- **Singular:** The <u>cat</u> thinks **it** can sleep all day.

- **Plural:** <u>Brianna and Madeline</u> know that **they** are sisters.

- **Male:** <u>Brian</u> helped **his** family cook breakfast.
  Female: <u>Jennifer</u> read **her** story to the class.

Practice **Write a pronoun to replace the underlined noun in each sentence.**

1. <u>Jody and I</u> raced our bikes across the park. _____

2. On Saturday, <u>Michael and Anthony</u> went swimming. _____

3. <u>Mom</u> was very surprised with the gifts. _____

4. I saw <u>Brian's</u> poster on the wall. _____

 **Apply** Circle the singular pronouns, and underline the plural pronouns in the paragraph.

I thought rabbits and hares were the same because they look alike. You would not believe the differences between them. A hare's fur is special. It turns white in the winter. The fur of rabbits changes from brown to gray with the seasons. A mother rabbit will build a nest for her babies, while hares are born on the ground. If we were to see rabbits in the wild, they would be with a group, but hares live alone. It has been fun for me to learn about these animals.

Find two sentences in "Hungry Little Hare" that use pronouns. Write each sentence on the blank line, and circle the pronoun. Write S above the pronoun if it is singular and P if it is plural.

5. _____

_____

6. _____

_____

Name _____ **Date** _____

/ow/ spelled ow and *ou_*

Focus The /ow/ sound can be spelled *ow* and *ou_*.

Practice **Read the sentence. Change the word in the box to make a new rhyming word that completes the sentence. Write the new word on the line.**

1. | **brown** | The queen's _____ is made of gold and jewels.

2. | **found** | Worms and other animals live under

the _____.

3. | **couch** | A baby kangaroo stays in its mother's

_____.

4. | **town** | I knew Eric was not happy when I saw the

_____ on his face.

5. | **chowder** | Suki likes to use lotion and _____ after her bath.

6. | **round** | The phone makes a funny _____ when it rings.

Read the sentence. Circle the word that completes each sentence. Write the word on the line.

7. The baby weighed eight _____ when it was born.

   a. pownds   **b.** pounds   **c.** ponds   **d.** puondz

8. When our dog gets upset he starts to _____.

   a. growl   **b.** ground   **c.** groul   **d.** ghrowl

9. The _____ cheered when our team won the game.

   a. crod   **b.** croud   **c.** croawd   **d.** crowd

10. Erin spilled milk on her new _____.

   a. blouse   **b.** blows   **c.** blues   **d.** bluos

Read each hint. Fill in the blank with *ow* or *ou* to complete the word.

11. A small animal that squeaks and likes cheese **m**_____**se**

12. Has petals and a stem **fl**_____**er**

13. Can use one to dry off after swimming **t**_____**el**

14. Something you can sit on **c**_____**ch**

15. Something a ball does **b**_____**nce**

16. Something a wolf is known to do **h**_____**l**

Prefix *mis-*

Focus

- A prefix is added to the beginning of a word and changes the meaning of that word.

- The prefix *mis-* means "bad," "wrong," or "incorrectly."

Example:

mis + spell = misspell (to spell wrong or incorrectly)

Practice Add the prefix *mis-* to the base words below. Write the new word on the first line. Then write the meaning of the new word.

Base Word	New Word	New Meaning
1. count	_____	_____
2. behave	_____	_____
3. match	_____	_____
4. place	_____	_____

Apply Write two sentences using the new words above.

5. _____

6. _____

Prefix *mid-*

Focus
- A prefix is added to the beginning of a word and changes the meaning of that word.
- The prefix *mid-* means "middle."

Example:

mid + year = midyear (in the middle of the year)

Practice Add the prefix *mid-* to the base words below. Write the new word on the first line. Then write the meaning of the new word.

Base Word	New Word	New Meaning
1. day	_____	_____
2. week	_____	_____

Apply Fill in the blank with the prefix *mis-* or *mid-* to create a new word that completes the sentence.

3. Did I _____ understand your directions to the game?

4. The employee worked on her _____ year review.

5. We have a _____ morning recess break at school.

6. It is easy to _____ count when you have a lot of items.

Selection Vocabulary

cautiously (kô' shəs lē) *adv.* With care. (page 112)

delicate (del' i kit) *adj.* Not strong. (page 117)

startled (stär' təld) *v.* Past tense of **startle:** to surprise. (page 113)

gratefully (grāt' fəl ē') *adv.* In a way that is full of thanks. (page 116)

reeds (rēdz) *n.* Plural of **reed:** tall grass. (page 112)

bank (bangk) *n.* The land along a stream. (page 110)

stubby (stub' ē) *adj.* Short and thick. (page 113)

admired (əd mīrd') *v.* Past tense of **admire:** to look at gratefully and with pleasure. (page 117)

temper (tem' pûr) *n.* Mood. (page 111)

glossy (glo' sē) *adj.* Bright and shiny. (page 106)

1. not strong _____

2. short and thick _____

3. mood _____

4. bright and shiny _____

5. with care _____

6. tall grasses _____

7. in a way that is full of thanks _____

8. the land along a stream _____

9. looked at gratefully and with pleasure _____

10. surprised _____

Selection Vocabulary

 Apply Write a vocabulary word from the box on the line to complete each sentence.

glossy	**startled**	**delicate**	**temper**	**cautiously**
reeds	**bank**	**gratefully**	**admired**	**stubby**

11. The bittern hid in the _____.

12. Julio has a bad _____.

13. The river _____ was muddy and wet.

14. Steven _____ accepted the gift.

15. My dad _____ the picture.

16. I was _____ by the loud noise.

17. Maria brushed her _____ hair.

18. The hare _____ poked its head out from a hole in the meadow.

19. Her dress was trimmed with _____ lace.

20. That dog has a _____ white tail.

21. Who has a bad *temper* in the story? _____

22. Who hid in the *reeds*? _____

23. Who do you think is the most *admired* character?

_____

Why?_____

_____

24. Which character would you describe as *delicate*?

_____

25. At one time, Nganga had only *glossy*,
black feathers. How did Cow change this?

_____

_____

_____

26. Why did Cow *gratefully* thank Nganga?

_____

_____

_____

Classify and Categorize

- Readers create different headings, or **categories**, based on what they have read.
- Readers then **classify** the information by placing details into appropriate **categories**.

Classify the animals in the box by writing the animal name under the category where it belongs.

polar bear	octopus	guinea fowl	crab spider
leaf insect	masked crab	cuttlefish	sea dragon

Land Animals   **Sea Animals**

_____   _____

_____   _____

_____   _____

_____   _____

1. **crab spider:** changes color to match flowers

2. **cuttlefish:** stripes can fade, leaving it one color

3. **leaf insect:** stays safe because other animals think it is a leaf

4. **katydid:** looks like a leaf to fool other animals

5. **guinea fowl:** spots help it blend in and hide

6. **sea dragon:** other animals go by thinking it is seaweed

7. **octopus:** changes color and can go from smooth to rough to blend in

8. **sargassum fish:** fools animals by looking like seaweed

Uses mimicry to hide

Uses colors and patterns to hide

_____   _____

_____   _____

_____   _____

_____   _____

Responding to Literature

Think Audience: **Who** will read your response to literature?

_____

Purpose: **What** is your reason for writing a response to literature?

_____

Prewriting Use the story map below to plan your response to literature. Fill in the main events from the beginning, middle, and end of the story.

Plot

Beginning (problem)	Middle (events)	Ending (how problem is solved)

Revising — Use this checklist to revise.

☐ Did you answer the question posed by your teacher?

☐ Does every sentence support your topic?

☐ Were any details left out that need to be added?

☐ Are your sentences in the correct order?

Editing/Proofreading — Use this checklist to correct mistakes.

☐ Is every word spelled correctly?

☐ Does every sentence and proper noun begin with a capital letter?

☐ Does every sentence end with the correct punctuation mark?

☐ Did you use possessive nouns and pronouns correctly?

Publishing — Use this checklist to prepare for publication.

☐ Write or type a neat copy of your response to literature.

☐ Include an illustration of one of the events in the story.

/ow/ spelled *ow, ou_*

Focus
- The /ow/ sound sounds like the word *cow* or *out*.
- It can be spelled *ow* and *ou_*.

Practice **Sort the spelling words under the correct heading.**

The /ow/ sound spelled *ow*

1. _____   4. _____

2. _____   5. _____

3. _____

The /ow/ sound spelled *ou_*

6. _____   9. _____

7. _____   10. _____

8. _____

Word List
1. ouch
2. hour
3. now
4. loud
5. crowd
6. down
7. sound
8. town
9. howl
10. round

Challenge Words
11. birdhouse
12. outside
13. shower
14. powder
15. blouse

11. grouch _____

12. cow _____

13. crown _____

14. found _____ _____

15. fowl _____

Visualization Strategy Circle the correct spelling for the following words. Then write the correctly spelled word on the line.

16. lowd   loud   _____

17. croud   crowd   _____

18. hour   ower   _____

Possessive Nouns

Focus
- A **noun** is a person, a place, or a thing.
- A **possessive word** shows ownership.
- A **possessive noun** ends in an apostrophe s ('s).
- A **plural possessive noun** ends in just an apostrophe (').

Examples:

Singular: *Jennifer's* mother works at the library.

Plural: The *books'* covers were torn.

Practice **Write the possessive form of the noun in parentheses ( ) on the line.**

1. I played with my _____ pet hamster. (friend)

2. The _____ dresses were green. (girls)

3. _____ brother knows a lot of magic tricks.
(Megan)

4. My _____ saddle is brand-new. (horse)

5. The _____ suggestion was very helpful. (librarian)

6. _____ dog is a beagle. (Sean)

Possessive Pronouns

Practice **Circle the correct pronoun to replace the underlined noun.**

1. Andrew's treasure map was buried in the yard. (He, His)

2. We went to Beth's house after school yesterday. (she, her)

3. The peacock's feathers were very colorful. (Its, You)

4. Jessica's bike is just like mine. (She, Her)

5. I like to listen to Zach's radio. (his, he)

6. My dog's leash is yellow. (Your, Its)

7. Lisa's home is next door to the bank. (Her, She)

8. The windows' locks are broken. (Its, Their)

/o͞o/, /oo/, and /ow/

Focus
• The /o͞o/ sound can be spelled using *oo*, *u*, *u_e*, *_ew*, or *_ue*.
• The /oo/ sound is spelled *oo*.
• The /ow/ sound can be spelled *ow* or *ou_*.

Practice **Use a word from the box to complete each sentence.**

hoop	**foot**	**truth**	**glued**
flute	**loud**	**allowed**	**chew**

1. I _____ the sheets of paper together.

2. Always tell the _____.

3. Eric was not _____ to play in the rain.

4. He threw the basketball into the _____.

5. It is important to _____ your food slowly.

6. Hannah is learning how to play the _____.

7. The _____ noise hurt my ears.

8. Jesse hurt his _____ when he slipped on the ice.

 **Apply** Circle the correct spelling for each word, and then write the word on the line.

9. knew   nue   _____

10. toob   tube   _____

11. raccoon   racune   _____

12. house   howse   _____

13. dewty   duty   _____

14. stude   stood   _____

15. true   trew   _____

16. arownd   around   _____

17. flower   flouer   _____

18. shook   shewk   _____

19. zoom   zume   _____

20. nuze   news   _____

21. toun   town   _____

22. tuna   tewna   _____

23. cloo   clue   _____

24. flute   floot   _____

Inflectional Endings and Comparative Ending -er

Focus

- The inflectional endings -ing and -ed can be added to a base word. The meaning of the word is not changed, only the form and function.
- The ending -ing lets you know something is happening now.
- The ending -ed lets you know something has already happened.
- The comparative ending -er shows a comparison between two things.

Practice   Add -ing and -ed to the following words. Write each new word on the line.

1. walk _____   _____

2. work _____   _____

3. help _____   _____

Add -er to the following words. Write the new word on the line.

4. fast _____

5. young _____

6. strong _____

Irregular Plurals

- Plural words show that there is more than one.
  Adding -s or -es to a word makes it a regular plural.

- Irregular plurals still mean that there is more than one. Instead of adding an -s or -es, the entire word is changed to make it plural.

Example:

    man   men

- Some words stay the same even when there is more than one.

Example:

    deer   deer

Draw a line to match the singular word to its irregular plural.

1. woman   **a.** people

2. person   **b.** women

3. tooth   **c.** teeth

Circle the correct word to complete each sentence.

4. My (foots   feet) fit perfectly in my new shoes.

5. A large flock of (sheep   sheeps) grazed in the field.

6. The (shelves   shelfes) were covered with dust.

Selection Vocabulary

Focus

unaware (un' ə wâr') *adj.* Not watchful or mindful. (page 132)

wariest (wâr' ē ist) *adj.* Most watchful or careful. (page 136)

stream (strēm) *n.* A small body of flowing water. (page 140)

protective (prə tek' tiv) *adj.* Keeps out of danger or away from harm. (page 134)

unnoticed (un nō' tisd) *adj.* Not seen or observed. (page 132)

coloration (kə' lə rā' shən) *n.* The way something is colored. (page 134)

wading (wād' ing) *adj.* Able to walk through water. (page 142)

imitator (im' i tā' tûr) *n.* One who copies something or someone. (page 139)

available (ə vā' lə bəl) *adj.* Being in the area and ready to use. (page 132)

natural (nach' ər əl) *adj.* Acting on information one is born with. (page 132)

Write the definitions for the vocabulary words below.

1. protective _____

2. available _____

3. coloration _____

4. stream _____

5. wading _____

6. unaware _____

7. natural _____

8. unnoticed _____

9. imitator _____

10. wariest _____

Apply Circle *Yes* if the boldfaced definition for the underlined word makes sense. Circle *No* if the boldfaced definition does not make sense.

11. Kendal loved to sit and read beside the <u>stream</u>.

small body of flowing water .... Yes   No

12. The mouse was <u>unaware</u> of the owl.

acting on information it was born with .... Yes   No

13. I keep my umbrella <u>available</u> for rainy days.

in the area and ready to use .... Yes   No

14. The <u>coloration</u> of my book makes it hard to read.

one who copies something or someone .... Yes   No

15. Many animals have the ability to go <u>unnoticed</u>.

keep out of danger or away from harm .... Yes   No

16. Jenna's sister is an <u>imitator</u>, always acting like Jenna.

one who copies someone .... Yes   No

17. When doing science experiments, you must wear <u>protective</u> glasses.

most watchful or careful .... Yes   No

18. It is <u>natural</u> for animals to hide from their enemies.

not seen or observed .... Yes   No

19. Did you see that dog walking through the water in the stream?

_____

20. Stacy was not mindful that she was stepping on flowers.

_____

21. Allison might be the most careful person I know.

_____

22. The animals on the hillside remained unobserved.

_____

23. Samantha enjoyed taking walks by the small body of flowing water.

_____

24. The young girl was pretending to be a cat; she was a person who copies something.

_____

Types of Camouflage

Look back over the selections you have read. Name some of the animals, and tell how they camouflage themselves.

Animal	Camouflage
1.	
2.	
3.	

4. Which animals use the same kind of camouflage?

_____

_____

5. Which animals use a different way to camouflage itself?

_____

_____

6. Can you name other animals that use camouflage?

_____

_____

7. Which animals would you like to learn more about?

_____

_____

8. How can you learn more about these animals?

_____

_____

Comparing and Contrasting

Think Audience: **Who** will read your comparing and contrasting paragraphs? _____

Purpose: **What** is your reason for writing comparing and contrasting paragraphs? _____

Prewriting Use the Venn diagram below to plan your comparing and contrasting paragraphs. Write comparisons in the overlapping section of the diagram. Then write contrasts in the outer sections.

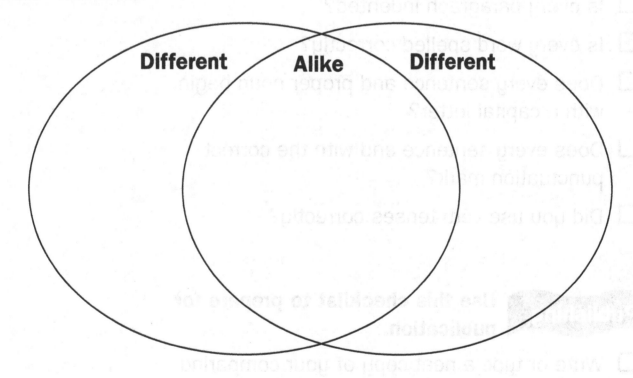

Different   **Alike**   **Different**

Revising — Use this checklist to revise.

☐ Does every sentence support your topic?

☐ Did you use descriptive details?

☐ Did you vary the beginnings of your sentences?

☐ Did you use comparing and contrasting clue words?

Editing/Proofreading — Use this checklist to correct mistakes.

☐ Is every paragraph indented?

☐ Is every word spelled correctly?

☐ Does every sentence and proper noun begin with a capital letter?

☐ Does every sentence end with the correct punctuation mark?

☐ Did you use verb tenses correctly?

Publishing — Use this checklist to prepare for publication.

☐ Write or type a neat copy of your comparing and contrasting paragraphs.

☐ Include illustrations of the comparisons and contrasts.

Review: /o͞o/, /oo/, /ow/

Focus

- The /o͞o/ sound sounds like the word *moo*. It can be spelled *oo, u, u_e, _ew,* and *_ue*.

- The /oo/ sound sounds like the word *look*. It is spelled *oo*.

- The /ow/ sound sounds like the word *now*. It can be spelled *ow* and *ou_*.

Word List

1. blue
2. rude
3. frown
4. cookie
5. plow
6. count
7. duty
8. cool
9. scout
10. books

Challenge Words

11. raccoon
12. snowplow
13. football
14. townhouse
15. rescue

Practice **Sort the spelling words under the correct heading.**

The /o͞o/ sound

1. _____   3. _____

2. _____   4. _____

The /oo/ sound

5. _____   6. _____

The /ow/ sound

7. _____   9. _____

8. _____   10. _____

Review: /o͞o/, /oo/, /ow/

Apply **Consonant-Substitution Strategy** Replace the underlined letter or letters with the new letter or letters to make a spelling word.

11. <u>c</u>ooks + b = _____

12. <u>tr</u>ue + bl = _____

13. scou<u>r</u> + t = _____

14. <u>d</u>own + fr = _____

15. ru<u>le</u> + d = _____

16. d<u>ue</u> + ty = _____

Rhyming Strategy Write the spelling word that rhymes with each word below. The spelling word will have the same /o͞o/, /oo/, or /ow/ spelling pattern as the rhyming word.

17. mount _____

18. fool _____

19. rookie _____

20. brow _____

Verb Tenses

Focus

- Finding the right verb and using the right tense of the verb is important when speaking and writing.

Rules:

- A **present-tense** verb tells about something that is happening now.

- A **past-tense** verb tells about something that happened in the past.

- A **future-tense** verb tells about something that will happen in the future.

- Some verbs do not add -*ed* to change from present to past tense. They change in other ways.

Example:

    I **sing.**   I **sang.**

Examples:

- I **walk** to school.

- I **walked** to school yesterday.

- I **will walk** to school tomorrow.

Practice   **Write the past and future tense for each verb on the lines.**

Present Tense	Past Tense	Future Tense
1. look	_____	_____
2. grow	_____	_____
3. drive	_____	_____

Apply **Complete each sentence with the correct tense of the boldfaced verb.**

4. I **gave** today. Next week I will _____.

5. Yesterday they **fought**. Today they _____.

6. We **are** happy. Last week we _____ happy.

7. Last month I **sang**. Tomorrow I will _____.

8. I can **throw** the ball. Yesterday I _____ the ball.

Write the correct verb tense to replace the underlined verb.

9. I will <u>sang</u> loudly at choir practice. _____

10. Tomorrow Ann will <u>rode</u> with us to school.

_____

11. When it snowed, our cat <u>come</u> inside. _____

12. Yesterday, there <u>is</u> nowhere to play. _____

13. Next year I will <u>am</u> in third grade. _____

14. Make sure to <u>looked</u> for cars before crossing the street.

_____

/aw/ spelled *aw* and *au_*

Focus The /aw/ sound can be spelled with *aw* and *au_*.

Practice **Read each sentence. Circle the word that correctly completes the sentence.**

1. Kirsten likes to paint and _____.
a. drau   **b.** draw   **c.** draue   **d.** drah

2. The train _____ us to be late.
a. caused   **b.** cawse   **c.** caosed   **d.** cawzd

3. The kitten licked its _____.
a. pah   **b.** paw   **c.** pau   **d.** pua

4. What time will they _____ the space shuttle?
a. lawnch   **b.** luwnch   **c.** lahntch   **d.** launch

5. Will you please help me _____ the firewood?
a. hall   **b.** hawl   **c.** haul   **d.** howl

6. We had a picnic on the _____.
a. lawn   **b.** laun   **c.** luwn   **d.** lahn

7. Ms. Wilhem washed the _____ last night.
a. lawndri   **b.** lawndree   **c.** laundry   **d.** landrie

Apply **Write *au* or *aw* in each blank to make a word that completes the sentence.**

8. My favorite flavor of jelly is str_____berry.

9. The marks on the tree were made by a bear's sharp

cl_____s.

10. E. B. White is the _____thor of the book *Charlotte's Web.*

11. There was too much tomato s_____ce on the pizza.

12. Janelle thought the movie was _____ful.

13. Most babies cr_____l before they learn to walk.

14. My aunt wears a sh_____l when it is cold outside.

Write a rhyming word for each word below.

15. lawn   _____

16. pause   _____

17. jaw   _____

18. haul   _____

19. vault   _____

20. squawk   _____

Suffixes -er and -ness

Focus
- A suffix is added to the end of a base word. Adding a suffix changes the meaning of the word.
- The suffix -ness means "the state of being."

Example:

dark + ness = darkness (the state of being dark)

- The suffix -er can mean "one who."

Example:

paint + er = painter (one who paints)

Practice Add the suffixes -er and -ness to the base words below, and write the new words. Then write the meaning of each new word.

1. work + er = _____ Meaning: _____

2. late + ness = _____ Meaning: _____

3. teach + er = _____ Meaning: _____

4. still + ness = _____ Meaning: _____

5. sleepy + ness = _____

Meaning: _____

6. sing + er = _____ Meaning: _____

 **Add the suffix -er or -ness to a word from the box before writing it on the line.**

ill	play	dark	kind	sad
swim	bright	speak	calm	grade

7. Chicken pox is an example of an _____.

8. It was easy to see John's _____ by his frown.

9. We need one more _____ for the soccer team.

10. My flashlight helped me walk in the _____.

11. I had to cover my eyes from the _____ of the sun.

12. I want to be a good _____ because I love the water so much.

13. I am a second _____ this year.

14. We get to listen to a guest _____ every Friday.

15. The sailors were pleased by the _____ of the sea.

16. _____ is the theme for Unit 1.

Write four sentences using the words in the box. Use each word only once.

worker	lateness	teacher	stillness

17. _____

18. _____.

19. _____.

20. _____.

Word Analysis • *Skills Practice 2*

Selection Vocabulary

Focus **cave** (kāv) *n.* A natural hole in the ground or in the side of a mountain. (page 164)

mountain (moun' tən) *n.* A mass of land that rises very high above the surrounding area. (page 163)

trembling (trem' bling) *v.* Shaking with cold, fear, anger, or weakness. (page165)

avalanche (av' ə lanch') *n.* Stones or snow rolling down a mountain. (page 165)

leaping (lēp' ing) *v.* Jumping. (page 163)

puffing (puf' ing) *v.* Breathing in short breaths. (page 163)

afraid (ə frād') *adj.* Feeling fear. (page 165)

screamed (skrēmd) *v.* Past tense of **scream:** to make a loud, shrill cry or sound. (page 167)

shadow (shad' ō) *n.* A dark area or figure made when rays of light are blocked by a person or thing. (page 166)

brave (brāv) *adj.* Able to face danger or pain without fear. (page 162)

Draw a line from the vocabulary word on the left to its correct definition on the right.

1. trembling

a. able to face danger or pain without fear

2. screamed

b. a natural hole in the ground or in the side of a mountain

3. leaping

c. stones or snow rolling down a mountain

4. shadow

d. breathing in short breaths

5. brave

e. feeling fear

6. mountain

f. made a loud, shrill cry or sound

7. avalanche

g. jumping

8. cave

h. a mass of land that rises very high above the surrounding area

9. puffing

i. shaking with cold, fear, anger, or weakness

10. afraid

j. a dark area or figure made when rays of light are blocked by a person or thing

Selection Vocabulary • *Skills Practice 2*

 **Apply** Write a vocabulary word in each blank to complete the sentence.

Frog and Toad wanted to be _____ together.

They were not _____ as they began their adventure

up the _____. Frog was _____ over

rocks, and Toad was _____ behind him. A snake in

a _____ left them _____ with fear.

Then the _____ sent them running away. Finally,

a hawk's _____ caused them to run home as they

_____ "We are not afraid!" Frog and Toad stayed

at home a long time feeling brave.

Write a sentence for five of the vocabulary words.

11. _____

_____

_____

12. _____

_____

_____

13. _____

_____

_____

14. _____

_____

_____

15. _____

_____

_____

Interview

What questions will you ask in your interview about a brave act? On these pages, write the questions you will use. As you ask each question during the interview, use the lines below the question to take notes about the answers.

1. **Question:** _____

   _____

   Answer: _____

   _____

2. **Question:** _____

   _____

   Answer: _____

   _____

3. **Question:** _____

   _____

   Answer: _____

   _____

4. Question: _____

_____

Answer: _____

_____

_____

5. Question: _____

_____

_____

Answer: _____

_____

_____

6. Question: _____

_____

_____

Answer: _____

_____

_____

Name _____ **Date** _____

Writing a Personal Letter

Think **Audience: Who** will read your letter?

_____

Purpose: What is your reason for writing a letter?

_____

Prewriting **Use this graphic organizer to plan the body of your letter.**

1. Start with the date and the word *Dear,* and then add the person's name.	
2. Explain the topic of your letter.	
3. Tell details about the topic.	
4. Choose a personal closing. It could be *Love,* or *Your friend.*	

Revising   Use this checklist to revise.

☐ Is the topic of your letter clear?

☐ Did you leave out anything that you want to put in your letter?

☐ Did you include descriptions of the events?

☐ Did you tell about the things you did?

☐ Does your letter sound personal and friendly?

Editing/Proofreading   Use this checklist to correct mistakes.

☐ Did you use commas correctly?

☐ Is every word or special term spelled correctly?

☐ Does each sentence begin with a capital letter and end with the correct punctuation mark?

☐ Does every name begin with a capital letter?

☐ Could you use other words to give more detail?

Publishing   Use this checklist to prepare for publication.

☐ Read your letter one more time. Make sure all the parts of a letter are included.

☐ Write or type a neat copy of your letter.

☐ Sign your letter.

☐ Address an envelope to mail your letter.

/aw/ spelled *aw, au_*

Focus

- The /aw/ sound sounds like the word *saw*.
- Two ways it can be spelled are *aw* and *au_*.

Practice **Sort the spelling words under the correct heading.**

/aw/ spelled *aw*

1. _____

2. _____

3. _____

4. _____

5. _____

/aw/ spelled *au_*

6. _____   9. _____

7. _____   10. _____

8. _____

Word List

1. hawk
2. sauce
3. thaw
4. draw
5. launch
6. crawl
7. yawn
8. author
9. cause
10. vault

Challenge Words

11. squawk
12. daunting
13. strawberry
14. because
15. audience

/aw/ spelled *aw, au_*

Apply **Visualization Strategy** Circle the correct spelling for each spelling word. Write the correct spelling on the line.

11. sawce   sauce   _____

12. thaw   thau   _____

13. draw   drawe   _____

14. cawse   cause   _____

Meaning Strategy Use the meaning clue to write the correct spelling word on each line.

15. a large place to store money or other valuables   _____

16. to make something take off or start   _____

17. a kind of large bird   _____

18. to move forward on the hands and knees   _____

19. someone who writes a book   _____

20. to open the mouth and take a deep breath when sleepy   _____

Capitals and Commas in Letter Greetings/Closings

- The beginning of a friendly letter is called the *greeting* or *salutation.*
- The first word begins with a capital letter.
- A comma is written after the name in the greeting.

Example:

> **D**ear Frog,

- The end of a friendly letter is called the closing.
- The first word begins with a capital letter.
- A comma is written after the closing.
- The sender's name is written beneath the closing.

Example:

> **L**ove,
>
> Toad

Insert commas for the possible greetings and closings for a friendly letter.

1. Dear Oscar _____

2. Respectfully _____
Oliver

3. Best wishes _____
Nola

4. My dear Nina _____

March 16, 2008

dear frog

   I am glad to have a brave friend like you. You were not afraid

to climb the mountain. I tried to be brave when the snake wanted

to eat us for lunch, even though I could not stop trembling! The

avalanche and the hawk were scary, but lucky for us we got away.

I felt brave with you when I was hiding in bed and you were in the

closet. You are my best friend!

                                              love

                                              toad

/aw/ spelled *augh* and *ough*

Focus The /aw/ sound can be spelled with *augh* and *ough*.

Practice Write the word from the box that best completes each sentence.

thought	taught	cough	naughty

1. Brittany _____ the movie started at five o'clock.

2. Our _____ dog chewed the newspaper.

3. Mr. Owens _____ me how to play chess.

4. I have a bad _____ with my cold.

Apply Use the letters in parentheses to make a word with the /aw/ spelling pattern.

5. (t, f) _____

6. (d, e, t, r) _____

7. (b, t) _____

8. (t, c) _____

/aw/ spelled *all* and *al*

Practice Read the word in the box. Then read the sentence. Change the word in the box to make a new rhyming word. Write the new word on the line.

1. **tall** I threw the _____ to Joshua.

2. **walk** There was dust from the _____ on my eraser.

3. **call** Be careful not to _____ into the water.

4. **stalk** William can _____ to his friends on the phone.

Apply Circle the correct spelling for each set of words.

5. walet   wallet

6. almost   allmost

7. halway   hallway

8. walked   wallked

Suffixes -*ly* and -*y*

Focus

- A suffix is added to the end of a base word. Adding a suffix changes the meaning of the word.
- The suffix -*ly* means "in a certain way."

Example:

  slow + ly = slowly (in a slow way)

- The suffix -*y* means "full of."

Example:

  rain + y = rainy (full of rain)

Practice Add -*ly* or -*y* to the following words. Write the new word on the line.

1. nice + ly = _____

2. brave + ly = _____

3. deep + ly = _____

4. leaf + y = _____

5. dirt + y = _____

6. boss + y = _____

Apply Add -*ly* or -*y* to the base word in parentheses ( ) to complete the sentence.

7. (*fuss*) My baby sister gets _____ when she is hungry.

8. (*neat*) Write your name _____ on the paper.

Suffix -ed

- A suffix is added to the end of a base word. Adding a suffix changes the meaning of the word.

- The suffix -ed shows that something has already happened. It changes the tense of the word from present to past tense.

Example:

> play + ed = played (past tense of *play*)

- When a base word has a short vowel followed by a consonant, the consonant is usually doubled before adding -ed.

Example:

> stop + ed = stopped (past tense of *stop*)

Practice   Add the suffix -ed to the following words. Make sure to double the final consonant.

Present Tense   **Past Tense**

1. spot + ed = _____

2. swat + ed = _____

3. kiss + ed = _____

4. nod + ed = _____

5. switch + ed = _____

6. fold + ed = _____

Selection Vocabulary

trickling (trik' ling) *v.* Flowing drop by drop. (page 182)

tulip (tōō' lip) *n.* A flower that is shaped like a cup. (page 178)

flooded (flud' əd) *v.* Past tense of **flood:** to cover with water. (page 181)

rumbling (rum' bling) *v.* Making a heavy, deep, rolling sound. (page 187)

numb (num) *adj.* Having no feeling. (page 186)

dikes (dīks) *n.* Plural of **dike:** a thick wall built to hold back water. (page 179)

gurgling (gûr' gling) *adj.* Sounding like a bubbling liquid. (page 182)

gushing (gush' ing) *v.* Pouring out suddenly. (page 184)

windmills (wind' milz) *n.* Plural of **windmill:** a machine that uses the power of the wind to turn sails. (page 178)

wheeled (hwēld) *v.* Past tense of **wheel:** to move or roll on wheels. (page 181)

Practice Write the vocabulary word that matches the descriptions below.

1. unable to feel anything _____

2. something used to prevent flooding _____

3. what you might have done to a cart _____

4. an interesting flower _____

5. filled with water_____

6. making a sound like thunder _____

7. very tall machines _____

8. flowing drop by drop _____

9. when water is rushing out really fast _____

10. sounding like a bubbling liquid _____

Selection Vocabulary • *Skills Practice 2*

 **Rewrite the following sentences. Replace each vocabulary word with its definition.**

11. The water was trickling from the faucet.

_____

_____

12. Hilda's house was flooded after the storm.

_____

_____

13. Playing in the snow for hours made my fingers numb.

_____

_____

14. There are many windmills in the country.

_____

_____

15. Janet's favorite flower is a tulip.

_____

_____

16. When the pipe under the sink burst, water was gushing onto the floor.

_____

_____

17. How do **windmills** work?

_____

_____

18. Why are **dikes** important?

_____

_____

19. What was **trickling** and making a **gurgling** sound in the story?

_____

20. What made the **rumbling** sound as it was **wheeled** down the road?

_____

21. Why was Peter's finger **numb**?

_____

_____

22. Why didn't the land become **flooded**?

_____

_____

Cause and Effect

Focus
- A **cause** is *why* something happens.
- An **effect** is *what* happens.

Practice Read each sentence. Write the *effect* (what happened) and the *cause* (why it happened).

1. Because it was hot, my friends and I went swimming.

Effect: _____

_____

Cause: _____

2. Because we wanted to be helpful, we picked up our toys.

Effect: _____

Cause: _____

3. It was my birthday, so we had a party.

Effect: _____

Cause: _____

4. Because it was raining, I put on my raincoat.

Effect: _____

Cause: _____

5. Effect: Peter got off his bike to see what was wrong.

Cause: _____

_____

6. Effect: All the people thanked Peter. They carried him on their shoulders, shouting, "Make way for the hero of Holland! The brave boy who saved our land!"

Cause: _____

_____

Write two sentences. Each sentence should show a cause and an effect.

7. _____

_____

_____

8. _____

_____

Write down a famous hero, such as George Washington, and then tell why you think that person is brave or shows bravery.

Famous Hero:

_____

Why is he or she brave?

_____

_____

_____

_____

Write down a community worker, such as a firefighter, and then tell why you think that person is brave or shows bravery.

Community Worker:

_____

Why is he or she brave?

_____

_____

Write down an everyday person, such as your grandmother, and then tell why you think that person is brave or shows bravery.

Everyday Person:

_____

Why is he or she brave?

_____

_____

_____

_____

Are you brave? Tell why you think you are brave. In what ways do you show bravery?

_____

_____

_____

_____

Responding to Literature

Think   **Audience: Who** will read your response to literature?

_____

Purpose: What is your reason for writing a response to literature?

_____

Prewriting   Use the cluster web below to plan your response to literature. Write the setting of the story in the center oval. Then write words and phrases that describe the setting in the outer ovals.

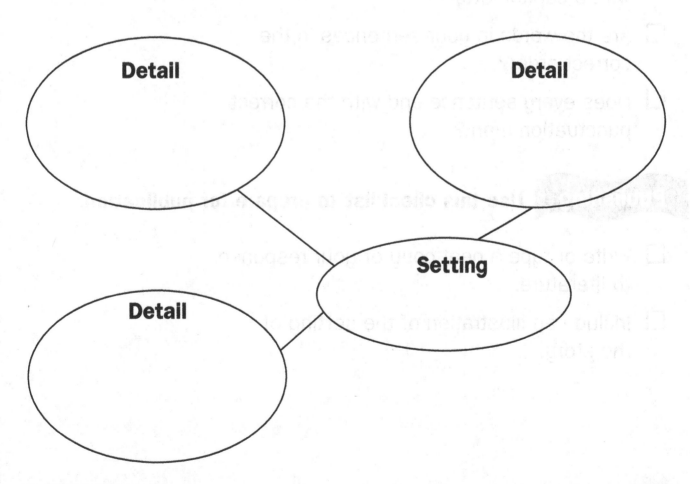

Revising Use this checklist to revise.

☐ Did you answer the questions posed by your teacher?

☐ Does every sentence support your topic?

☐ Were any details left out that need to be added?

☐ Are your sentences in the correct order?

Editing/Proofreading Use this checklist to correct mistakes.

☐ Is every word spelled correctly?

☐ Does every sentence and proper noun begin with a capital letter?

☐ Are the words in your sentences in the correct order?

☐ Does every sentence end with the correct punctuation mark?

Publishing Use this checklist to prepare for publication.

☐ Write or type a neat copy of your response to literature.

☐ Include an illustration of the setting of the story.

/aw/ spelled *augh, ough, all, al*

Focus
- The /aw/ sound sounds like the word *taught*.
- Some ways the /aw/ sound can be spelled include *augh, ough, all,* and *al*.

Practice   **Sort the spelling words under the correct heading.**

/aw/ spelled *augh*

1. _____   2. _____

/aw/ spelled *ough*

3. _____   4. _____

/aw/ spelled *all*

5. _____   7. _____

6. _____

/aw/ spelled *al*

8. _____   10. _____

9. _____

Word List
1. walk
2. overalls
3. bought
4. call
5. always
6. sought
7. taught
8. caught
9. halt
10. small

Challenge Words
11. daughter
12. chalk
13. thought
14. naughty
15. sidewalk

Apply **Rhyming Strategy** Write the spelling word or words that rhyme with each word below. The spelling word will have the same /aw/ spelling pattern as the rhyming word.

11. fought _____ _____

12. ball _____ _____

Consonant-Substitution Strategy Replace the underlined letter or letters with the new consonant to make a spelling word.

13. <u>t</u>alk + w = _____

14. <u>s</u>alt + h = _____

15. <u>c</u>aught + t = _____

16. <u>th</u>ought + b = _____

17. <u>t</u>all + sm = _____

18. al<u>so</u> + ways = _____

19. <u>so</u>ught + ta = _____

20. over<u>cast</u> + alls = _____

Word Order

- The words in a sentence must be in the correct order.
- Every complete sentence has a subject and a predicate. Usually the subject of the sentence comes first.

Practice   Underline the subject, and double-underline the predicate in each sentence.

1. My mom went shopping.

2. The pig is rolling around in the mud.

3. Yesterday, I had a spelling quiz.

4. Lily gave me a pretty dress for my birthday.

5. Five birds are sitting on the branch.

6. The clouds look dark and heavy today.

7. My class goes on a field trip to the zoo every year.

8. playing soccer and football I like.

_____

_____

9. is windy and cold it today.

_____

_____

10. new coat red and black Garrett's is.

_____

_____

11. are swimming the ducks in the pond.

_____

_____

12. time it what is?

_____

_____

The *ough* spelling pattern

Focus
- The *ough* spelling pattern has many different sounds.
- Adding the letter *t* to the end of the *ough* pattern makes the /aw/ sound.

Practice   **Use the words in the box to answer the questions.**

cough	through	dough	tough

1. Which word has the same vowel sound as *no?*

_____

2. Which word has the same vowel sound as *blue?*

_____

3. Which word has the same vowel sound as *saw?*

_____

4. Which word has the same vowel sound as *puff?*

_____

Add the given letter to the *ought* spelling
pattern. Write the new word on the line.

5. s + ought = _____

6. f + ought = _____

7. b + ought = _____

8. br + ought = _____

Circle the correct word to complete each sentence.

9. Marcia (bough, bought) a present for her grandma.

10. Do we have (enough, enought) pizza for everyone?

11. I (though, thought) the homework was due tomorrow.

12. The prince (fought, fough) the dragon and won.

13. Tracy used the (dought, dough) to bake bread.

14. (Althought, Although) I live close to the school, I still ride
the bus.

15. Jasmine (brought, bough) her tent on the camping trip.

16. The pirate (sough, sought) the treasure using a map.

Suffixes -less and -ful

Focus
- A suffix is added to the end of a base word. Adding a suffix changes the meaning of the word.
- The suffix -less means "without."

Example:

hope + less = hopeless (without hope)

- The suffix -ful means "full of."

Example:

joy + ful = joyful (full of joy)

Practice Add the suffix **-less** and then **-ful** to each of the base words below. Write each new word and then the new meaning of each new word.

Base Word	-less	New Meaning
1. fear	_____	_____
2. pain	_____	_____

Base Word	-ful	
3. care	_____	_____
4. hope	_____	_____

Prefixes and Suffixes as Syllables

Focus Adding a prefix or a suffix to a word adds a syllable to the word.

Practice Divide the following words into syllables.

1. restful _____

2. flawless _____

3. mistake _____

4. illness _____

5. unworthy _____

Apply Add a base word to the prefix or suffix in parentheses ( ). Divide the new word into syllables.

6. (mid) _____ _____

7. (ly) _____ _____

8. (er) _____ _____

9. (dis) _____ _____

10. (ing) _____ _____

Word Analysis • *Skills Practice 2*

Selection Vocabulary

Focus

transferred (trans fûrd') *v.* Past tense of **transfer:** to move something from one place to another. (page 206)

sprout (sprout) *v.* To begin to grow. (page 205)

burst (bûrst) *v.* To break open suddenly. (page 200)

courage (kûr' ij) *n.* The strength to overcome fear. (page 213)

clever (klev' ər) *adj.* Showing skill or ability. (page 208)

tended (ten' dəd) *v.* Past tense of **tend:** to take care of. (page 201)

blossom (blos' əm) *v.* To bloom. (page 205)

kingdom (king' dəm) *n.* A country ruled by a king or queen. (page 200)

worthy (wûr' ᵺē) *adj.* Having enough value; deserving. (page 212)

emperor (em' pə rûr) *n.* A ruler. (page 201)

Practice Fill in each blank with a vocabulary word from this lesson.

1. Everyone who lived in the _____ loved flowers.

2. Anything that Ping planted would _____.

3. Flowers would _____ into bloom.

4. The emperor was looking for someone _____ to take the throne.

5. Despite being _____ to better soil, the seed would not grow.

6. No matter what Ping did, the seed refused to

   _____.

7. Ping _____ to his seed in the empty pot.

8. Only Ping had the _____ to tell the truth.

9. This made Ping _____ of a great honor.

10. Ping became the new _____.

Apply   **List antonyms and synonyms for the vocabulary words listed below.**

Vocabulary words	Synonyms	Antonyms
11. clever	_____	_____
12. emperor	_____	_____
13. transferred	_____	_____
14. tended	_____	_____
15. blossom	_____	_____
16. worthy	_____	_____
17. sprout	_____	_____
18. burst	_____	_____

 Tell whether the boldfaced definition that is given for the underlined word in each sentence below makes sense. Circle *Yes* or *No*.

19. The <u>emperor</u> is powerful.
ruler ....Yes   No

20. Sam <u>transferred</u> the book to the library.
bloomed ....Yes   No

21. The flowers <u>blossom</u> in May.
bloom ....Yes   No

22. The lion wanted some <u>courage</u>.
strength to overcome fear ....Yes   No

23. The tulips began to <u>sprout</u>.
take care of ....Yes   No

24. Everyone in the <u>kingdom</u> liked the queen.
country ruled by a king or queen ....Yes   No

25. Amy <u>tended</u> to her garden every day.
showing skill or ability ....Yes   No

Writing a Fantasy

Think **Audience: Who** will read your fantasy?

_____

Purpose: What is your reason for writing your
fantasy?

_____

Prewriting **Use the graphic organizer below to brainstorm
ideas for your fantasy.**

Setting (where the story takes place)		**Characters** (people or animals in the story)
	Title (name of the story)	
Problem (something causing trouble)		**Solution** (how the problem is fixed)

Using Action and Describing Words

Use action and describing words to fill in the blanks in the sentences below.

1. Troy and his _____ dog went for a

   _____ walk today.

2. In the middle of the walk, something _____
   happened.

3. Troy's dog Butter started talking very _____.

4. Butter told Troy about a _____ field where
   there was a spaceship.

5. Butter and Troy _____ to the field.

6. They were playing on the spaceship when the spaceship

   _____ _____.

Apply **Use the lines below to list action and descriptive words that you could use in your fantasy.**

_____   _____

_____   _____

_____   _____

ough spelling pattern

Focus
- The spelling patterns *augh* and *ough* can make different sounds.
- The *ough* spelling pattern can sound like /aw/, /ō/, and /u̯/.

Practice **Sort the spelling words under the correct heading.**

Word List
1. cough
2. dough
3. fought
4. though
5. thought
6. rough
7. although
8. tough
9. ought
10. enough

Challenge Words
11. thoughtful
12. thorough
13. sourdough
14. brought
15. throughout

ough with the /aw/ sound

1. _____

2. _____

3. _____

4. _____

ough with the /ō/ sound

5. _____

6. _____

7. _____

ough with the /u̯/ sound

8. _____

9. _____

10. _____

Rhyming Strategy Find the spelling
word or words that rhyme with each
word below.

11. bought _____

12. enough _____ _____

Visualization Strategy Circle the correct spelling
for each word below. Then write the correct spelling
on the line.

13. coff   cough   _____

14. ought   aut   _____

15. though   thoe   _____

16. dogh   dough   _____

17. although   alltho   _____

18. enuff   enough   _____

19. thought   thawt   _____

20. tough   tugh   _____

Quotation Marks and Commas in Dialogue

Focus

- **Quotation marks** are used around the titles of stories, poems, and book chapters.

Example:

I like the story "The Empty Pot."

- A **quotation mark** is used right before and right after the words a speaker says.

Example:

"I have grown lots of flowers better than yours," Ping said.

- **Commas** are used to separate the quotation from the person who said it.

Example:

Donna said, "I love planting flowers."

- **Commas** are used after the word, before the end quotes.

Example:

"I want to grow the prettiest flower," said Julia.

Practice   **Read the sentences. Insert quotation marks and commas in the proper places.**

1. Joe said   I need to buy some carrots.

2. Charlotte sighed   Tomorrow is another day.

3. I will not walk my dog today   Leo said.

4. Recess is in five minutes my teacher said.

 **Apply** **Read the sentences. Insert quotation marks and commas in the proper places.**

5. My favorite story is Corduroy by Don Freeman.

6. Ron said I don't think this is the right house.

7. Will you feed my fish while I'm away at camp? asked Jeffrey.

8. The story I See Animals Hiding taught me about camouflage.

9. Anna asked Have you seen my kitten?

10. I love the poem Ants by Marilyn Singer.

11. We will have recess after our story said Mrs. Baker.

12. This is my favorite time of the day said Josh.

13. Brent exclaimed Come quick I found something!

14. Turn to page 97 in your text book commanded Mrs. Right.

15. Hurry up yelled my brother.

/oi/ spelled _oy and oi

Focus   /oi/ can be spelled with _oy and oi.

Practice   Write a letter on the line to create a word with the _oy spelling pattern. Then write the whole word on the line.

1. _____ oy   _____

2. _____ oy   _____

3. _____ oy   _____

4. _____ oy   _____

Write a letter on the lines to create a word with the oi spelling pattern. Then write the whole word on the line.

5. _____oi_____   _____

6. _____oi_____   _____

7. _____oi_____   _____

8. _____oi_____   _____

9. _____oi_____   _____

10. _____oi_____   _____

11. I need to b_____l the water before I put the pasta in the pot.

12. Is the new baby a girl or a b_____?

13. My little sister pulls my hair just to ann_____ me.

14. Can you p_____nt us in the right direction?

15. Mia likes to hike, and she also enj_____s sailing.

16. The princess was able to attend the r_____al ball.

17. Luke added a new quarter to his c_____n collection.

18. Actors in a play speak in loud v_____ces.

19. Tr_____ is my very best friend.

20. I hope the ants and bees will not sp_____l our picnic.

21. There is too much m_____sture in the basement.

22. The tornado destr_____ed everything along the coast.

23. My younger sister always av_____ds getting in trouble.

24. Rachel always sounds so j_____ful when she sings.

Multiple-Meaning Words

> **Focus**
>
> Multiple-meaning words are spelled and pronounced the same but have different meanings.
>
> **Example:**
>
> **bark**   Meaning #1: The sound a dog makes
>
> Meaning #2: The outer coating of a tree

Practice **Use the multiple-meaning words below to complete the sentences. Use each word twice.**

fan	duck	sink

1. Jonathan is a huge sports _____. The

_____ made a nice breeze that cooled us off.

2. Our raft will _____ if anything else is put on it.

It is important to wash your hands in the _____ before eating.

3. We threw crackers to the _____. Todd shouted,

"_____!" when the ball came toward me.

Apply **Read the two meanings for a multiple-meaning word. Write the words on the line.**

4. a vacation **or** to fall over something _____

5. an insect **or** to move in the air _____

Homophones

Focus Homophones are words that are pronounced the same, but they are spelled differently and have different meanings.

Example:

I can <u>see</u> a fish swimming in the <u>sea</u>.

Practice **Use these homophones to complete the sentences.**

sun	red	blew
son	read	blue

1. The wind _____ the kite. There was not a cloud in the

clear, _____ sky.

2. Our class _____ two books this week. Dalmatians rode

on the _____ firetruck.

3. The huge, yellow _____ rose in the morning sky. A boy

child is the _____ of his parents.

Apply **Read the two meanings for a pair of homophones. Write the two homophones on the lines.**

4. the number after seven _____

past tense of *eat* _____

Selection Vocabulary

Focus

rumble (rum' bəl) *n.* A heavy, deep, rolling sound. (page 244)

rugged (rug' id) *adj.* Rough and uneven. (page 224)

descents (di sents') *n.* Plural of **descent:** a downward slope. (page 225)

snowdrift (snō drift') *n.* Snow piled up by the wind. (page 233)

burrowed (bûr' ōd) *v.* Past tense of **burrow:** to dig. (page 233)

squinted (skwin' təd) *v.* Past tense of **squint:** to look with the eyes slightly closed. (page 240)

biting (bīt' ing) *adj.* Cold enough to sting. (page 227)

gusted (gust' əd) *v.* Past tense of **gust:** to blow wind or air suddenly and strongly. (page 231)

shifted (shif' təd) *v.* Past tense of **shift:** to change position. (page 231)

snapped (snapt) *v.* Past tense of **snap:** to move in a quick and sharp way. (page 231)

Write the definition for each vocabulary word.

1. rugged: _____

2. squinted: _____

3. shifted: _____

4. burrowed: _____

5. snapped: _____

6. rumble: _____

7. snowdrift: _____

8. gusted: _____

9. descents: _____

10. biting: _____

11. The Iditarod Race has a very _____ trail with some

steep _____.

12. Akiak jumped, pulled, and _____ when she tried
to break free.

13. To wait out the storm, Akiak _____ into the snow.

14. As the wind _____, the plane _____,
and the handler let go of the leash.

15. A _____ formed from the blowing snow.

16. Mick _____ against the _____ wind,
looking for a sign.

17. The _____ of the crowd's cheers welcomed
the team.

18. _____

_____

_____

_____

19. _____

_____

_____

_____

20. _____

_____

_____

_____

Sequence

> **Focus**
> - **Sequence** is the order in which events in a story occur. Writers often use time and order words to help readers understand the sequence of events.
> - **Time** words (*winter, today, night*) show the passage of time.
> - **Order** words (*first, next, finally*) show the order in which events happen.

Practice **Read this paragraph carefully. Underline the time words, and circle the order words.**

Seth gets up every morning at seven o'clock. Every morning he does the same things. He gets dressed first. Then he makes his bed. After that, he brushes his teeth. About fifteen minutes later, Seth is ready to eat breakfast.

Write about something you know how to do, such as making a sandwich. Make sure the sequence of events is clear.

_____

_____

_____

_____

_____

Reread "Akiak: A Tale from the Iditarod."
Write down four things that happened in the
story in the order they happened.

1. _____

_____

2. _____

_____

3. _____

_____

4. _____

_____

Draw a picture of each event in the boxes below.

Event 1	Event 2	Event 3	Event 4

Using Descriptive Dialogue

Practice Use action and descriptive words to fill in the blanks below.

1. "Come on, let's _____ to the field," Troy said.

2. Butter said, "Look at this _____ spaceship."

3. "Let's go inside and _____ at the

_____ controls," said Troy.

4. "I am going to _____ this button," said Butter.

5. "What is that _____ noise?" asked Troy.

Apply Use the lines below to write descriptive dialogue for your fantasy. Be sure to correctly use commas and quotation marks.

_____

_____

_____

_____

_____

_____

_____

Revising Use this checklist to revise.

☐ Does your fantasy have a beginning, a middle, and an end?

☐ Are the events in the correct order?

☐ Does the problem get solved at the end of the story?

Editing/Proofreading Use this checklist to correct mistakes.

☐ Is every word or special term spelled correctly?

☐ Did you capitalize the names of characters and places?

☐ Does every sentence start with a capital letter?

☐ Does every sentence end with the correct punctuation mark?

☐ Do your sentences begin in different ways?

Publishing Use this checklist to prepare for publication.

☐ Write or type a neat copy of your fantasy.

☐ Include a "Note from the Author" telling what you like best about your story.

☐ Draw a picture of the characters and setting.

/oi/ spelled *oi* and _*oy*

Focus
- The /oi/ sound sounds like the word *coil*.
- It can be spelled *oi* and _*oy*.

Practice **Sort the spelling words under the correct heading.**

/oi/ spelled *oi*

1. _____
2. _____
3. _____
4. _____
5. _____
6. _____

/oi/ spelled *oy*

7. _____
8. _____
9. _____
10. _____

Word List
1. join
2. spoil
3. annoy
4. choice
5. boys
6. point
7. coin
8. enjoy
9. boil
10. toy

Challenge Words
11. royal
12. appoint
13. moist
14. rejoice
15. oyster

Visualization Strategy Circle the correct spelling for each spelling word. Write the correct spelling on the line.

11. enjoy enjoi _____

12. boyal boil _____

13. choice choys _____

14. anoi annoy _____

15. boys boize _____

Rhyming Strategy Write the spelling word or words that rhyme with each word below. The spelling word will have the same /oi/ spelling pattern as the rhyming word.

16. loin _____ _____

17. joy _____

18. foil _____ _____

19. joint _____

20. rejoice _____

Using a Dictionary, a Glossary, and a Thesaurus

Focus
- A **dictionary** is a book that lists words and their definitions.
- A **glossary** is part of a book, usually at the end, that gives definitions for words that appear in that book.
- A **thesaurus** gives synonyms and antonyms for words.

Practice **Look up the following words in the glossary of *Student Reader*, Book 2 and in a dictionary. Write the guide words from each source.**

1. brave

      Glossary _____ _____

      Dictionary _____ _____

2. puffing

      Glossary _____ _____

      Dictionary _____ _____

3. rumble

      Glossary _____ _____

      Dictionary _____ _____

Apply   Now look up the following words in a thesaurus. Write a synonym and an antonym for each word.

4. brave

Synonym: _____

Antonym: _____

5. gloomy

Synonym: _____

Antonym: _____

6. stroll

Synonym: _____

Antonym: _____

7. silent

Synonym: _____

Antonym: _____

8. smile

Synonym: _____

Antonym: _____

Conjunctions

Focus
- A **conjunction** is a word that connects words or ideas. *And*, *or*, and *but* are conjunctions.

Example:

Rosa walked to the mailbox. She mailed the letter.

Rosa walked to the mailbox, **and** she mailed the letter.

Practice **Put an *X* next to the sentences that can be combined because they are about the same topic.**

1. The dog barked. He wagged his tail. _____

2. Jason ran home. The sun was shining. _____

3. Seth hit the ball. He ran to first base. _____

4. The car was going fast. We were eating lunch. _____

5. Nick went to the phone. He answered it. _____

6. I like to watch old movies. My brother likes to listen to

music. _____

7. Sean likes first grade. Harry went to preschool. _____

8. Nancy draws pictures of her friends. She gives them as

gifts. _____

 **Read the sentences. Write a conjunction (and, or, but) on the blank line to complete each sentence.**

9. We may skip to school, _____ we will not be late.

10. Susie will buy a birthday card, _____ she may make a card instead.

11. I am wearing a blue cap, _____ I am wearing a blue jacket today.

12. My teacher said it might rain tomorrow, _____ we are still going on our class field trip.

13. The cat loves to play with yarn, _____ she also plays with a ball.

14. Joe will read a book about cars, _____ he may read about dinosaurs.

Use the conjunction in parentheses ( ) to write your own sentence.

(and) _____

_____

(but) _____

(or) _____

Name _____ **Date** _____

/aw/ and /oi/

Focus
- /aw/ can be spelled *aw*, *au_*, *augh*, *ough*, *al*, and *all*.
- /oi/ can be spelled *_oy* and *oi*.

Practice **Use the words in the box to complete the sentences.**

employer	hallway	audience	rejoice
stalk	thought	lawn	caught

1. Max mows the _____ every Saturday.

2. Performing in front of an _____ can be scary.

3. I _____ when the teacher says it is time for recess.

4. Ava _____ the spelling test was today.

5. The _____ of celery was very crunchy.

6. You can find the bathroom down the _____.

7. My brother _____ the football and scored a touchdown.

8. An _____ pays you money to do a job.

Unscramble the following words, and then write each new word on the line. Underline the /aw/ or /oi/ spelling pattern in each word.

9. d c a l e l _____

10. d a i v o _____

11. t t a g u h _____

12. e b s e c u a _____

13. l w u a f _____

14. g b u o h t _____

15. t a o m l s _____

16. s e t r o d y _____

Circle the correct spelling for each word.

17. falling   fawling

18. decoi   decoy

19. thawt   thought

20. choice   choyse

21. cralling   crawling

22. fault   fawlt

Words with the Same Base

Focus

A base word is a word that can stand alone. A base word can give a clue to the meaning of other words in the word family.

Example:

base word: rain

word family: rainy, raining, rainstorm, rainfall

Practice   Write the base word for each word family below.

1. walks, walking, walkway

base word: _____

2. hands, handed, handful

base word: _____

3. birdcage, blackbird, birdcall

base word: _____

4. homemade, homeroom, homework

base word: _____

5. lighter, lightning, lighthouse

base word: _____

Circle the words in the same word family. Then write the base word the family shares on the line.

6. dashed   dusting   dashing

base word: _____

7. ants   anthill   attic

base word: _____

8. doghouse   doorbell   watchdog

base word: _____

9. trusted   twisted   twisting

base word: _____

10. lovable   lucky   luckiness

base word: _____

11. sunrise   sunset   morning

base word: _____

12. greatest   best   greater

base word: _____

Selection Vocabulary

 Focus **reservation** (re' zər vā' shən) *n.* Land where Native Americans live. (page 254)

mysterious (mis tēr' ē əs) *adj.* Difficult to understand or explain. (page 277)

shivered (shiv' ərd) *v.* Past tense of **shiver:** to shake or tremble. (page 254)

mountain lion (moun' tən lī' ən) *n.* A large wild cat that lives in the mountains. (page 264)

stomping (stom' ping) *v.* Walking heavily. (page 257)

qualified (kwol' ə fīd') *v.* Past tense of **qualify:** to be able to do a job or task. (page 261)

inform (in fôrm') *v.* To tell. (page 261)

terrific (tə rif' ik) *adj.* Wonderful. (page 282)

dreaded (dre' dəd) *v.* Past tense of **dread:** to be afraid of or anxious about something. (page 254)

swirling (swûr' ling) *v.* Spinning around. (page 270)

Practice Draw a line from each vocabulary word to its correct definition.

1. inform

2. swirling

3. dreaded

4. mysterious

5. shivered

6. stomping

7. mountain lion

8. terrific

9. qualified

10. reservation

a. a large wild cat that lives in the mountains

b. was afraid of or anxious about something

c. difficult to understand or explain

d. walking heavily

e. to tell

f. able to do a job or task

g. land where Native Americans live

h. spinning around

i. wonderful

j. shook or trembled

Selection Vocabulary • *Skills Practice 2*

Read the sentences below. Then rewrite each sentence, replacing the underlined words or phrases with vocabulary words.

11. Melinda <u>trembled</u> when she heard the lion's roar.

_____

_____

12. Mr. Thompson asked his students to <u>tell</u> him why they were late for class.

_____

_____

13. At night we can hear a <u>large wild cat that lives in the mountains</u> near our town.

_____

_____

14. I could see the snow <u>spinning around</u> in the street lights.

_____

_____

15. Heather had a <u>wonderful</u> idea.

_____

_____

16. Spider _____ giving his father the papers from school.

dreaded   inform   qualified   stomping

17. Many Native Americans live on a _____.

mysterious   mountain lion   terrific   reservation

18. His parents were very proud that he _____ for the spelling bee.

shivered   terrific   qualified   mysterious

19. Will was _____ his feet to get the snow off his boots.

stomping   swirling   informing   reservation

20. The small spider seemed to speak in a _____ way.

stomping   mysterious   swirling   qualified

Author's Purpose

Focus
- Understanding an author's purpose helps readers understand the story.
- Authors write to **entertain, inform,** and **persuade.**

Practice   **After each sentence, write the author's purpose.**

1. If we all help, we can make our city clean. _____

2. As the sun rose, the ocean sparkled like diamonds.

_____

3. This is the oldest fossil known to humans. _____

4. China is the country with the largest population.

_____

5. The silly puppy fell asleep in the drawer. _____

6. There are many reasons for people to stop littering.

_____

Apply Read the following story titles, and determine the author's purpose for each one. Then write your own story titles for each purpose.

7. "The Great Sleepover Mystery" _____

8. "Why Students Should Make the Rules" _____

9. "Zoo Animals" _____

10. "What I Did on My Summer Vacation" _____

11. "Paper Needs to Be Recycled Now" _____

12. "The History of North America" _____

13. Story Title: _____

_____

Author's Purpose: _____

14. Story Title: _____

Author's Purpose: _____

15. Story Title: _____

Author's Purpose: _____

Writing a Realistic Story

Think **Audience: Who** will read your story?

_____

Purpose: What is your reason for writing your story?

_____

Prewriting **Choose your main character. Write the character's name on the line. Then write a list of details about your main character.**

Main Character: _____

Details: _____

Fill in the story details on the story map.

Characters:
Setting:

PLOT

Beginning: Middle: End:

Narrator of the story (point of view):

Revising Use this checklist to revise.

☐ Are your characters and setting realistic?

☐ Could the events in your story really happen?

☐ Will your reader be able to follow your story?

☐ Did you use dialogue that shows how your characters think and feel?

Editing/Proofreading Use this checklist to correct mistakes.

☐ Is every word or special term spelled correctly?

☐ Did you use correct punctuation in the dialogue?

☐ Does every sentence start with a capital letter and end with the correct punctuation mark?

☐ Are there details you could add to make your story more exciting and realistic?

Publishing Use this checklist to prepare for publication.

☐ Give your story a title.

☐ Write or type a neat copy of your story.

☐ Include a drawing that shows a character or an event from your story.

Review: /aw/ spelled *aw*, *au_*, *augh*, *ough*, *all*, and *al*; /oi/ spelled *oi* and *_oy*

Focus
- The /aw/ sound can be spelled *aw*, *au_*, *augh*, *ough*, *all*, and *al*.
- The /oi/ sound can be spelled *oi* and *_oy*.

Practice Sort the spelling words under the correct heading.

The /aw/ sound

1. _____

2. _____

3. _____

4. _____

5. _____

6. _____

The /oi/ sound

7. _____

8. _____

9. _____

10. _____

Word List
1. lawn
2. haul
3. recall
4. stalk
5. thoughts
6. fault
7. voyage
8. noise
9. loyal
10. avoid

Challenge Words
11. ointment
12. walnut
13. hallway
14. employer
15. falling

Visualization Strategy Look at each word below. If the word is spelled correctly, write the word *correct* on the line. If the word is misspelled, write the correct spelling on the line.

11. stauck _____

12. thoughts _____

13. avoid _____

14. voiage _____

15. hough _____

16. fault _____

Proofreading Strategy Read the story below. Circle any misspelled words. Then write the correctly spelled word on the line.

I can reackal one time I heard a noyze on our front laughn. When I went outside to investigate, I noticed a strange dog tearing through our trash can. Just then, our loil dog Scout chased the rascal away. What a sight!

17. _____

18. _____

19. _____

20. _____

Compound Sentences

Focus
A **compound sentence** is made when two sentences with similar ideas are combined into one sentence. The sentences are connected with a conjunction.

Example:

Today I need to wash my clothes. Today I need to go to the grocery store.

Today I need to wash my clothes, **and** I need to go to the grocery store.

Practice **Read each sentence. Write C on the line next to the sentences that are compound.**

1. Mike and Joe went to camp. _____

2. Mike went to camp in San Diego, and Joe went to camp in

Colorado. _____

3. The boys swam in the lake, and they rode horses. _____

4. The best part about camp was telling stories by the fire.

_____

5. During the summer, my favorite activities are rafting and

running. _____

6. My family likes to go camping, but Joe's family likes to go to

the beach. _____

7. Josh took his dog for a walk, and _____

_____

8. The state of Georgia is above Florida, and _____

_____

9. Today I have two tests, but _____

_____

10. I do not know if I should take my dog, or _____

_____

11. I would like to take a lot of pictures during our vacation, but

_____

12. Lisa likes to talk on the phone, and _____

_____

13. My chore is to clean the living room, but _____

_____

14. Today I can eat pasta for dinner, or _____

_____

15. My birthday is in March, but _____

_____

/ō/, /ow/, /ū/, /ōō/, and /oo/

- The *ow* spelling pattern can make the /ō/ sound or the /ow/ sound.

- The *u*, *u_e*, *_ue*, and *_ew* spelling patterns can make the /ū/ and /ōō/ sounds.

- The *oo* spelling pattern can make the /ōō/ and /oo/ sounds.

Practice Write the following *ow* spelling pattern words under the correct sound, /ō/ or /ow/.

crowded shallow	yellow eyebrows	rookie groomer	booth football

/ō/

1. _____

2. _____

/ow/

3. _____

4. _____

Write the following *oo* spelling pattern words under the correct sound, /ōō/ or /oo/.

/ōō/

5. _____

6. _____

/oo/

7. _____

8. _____

Apply Unscramble the letters in parentheses ( ) to make a word with the given spelling pattern.

9. (r, c) _____ow

10. (g, d, l) _____ue_____

11. (h, s, p) _____oo_____

12. (f, r, l, e) _____ow_____

13. (r, g) _____ew

14. (t, t, h, r) _____u_____

15. (f, h) _____oo_____

16. (b, s, a) _____u_____e

Write a word for each spelling pattern listed below.

17. *ow* sounding like /ō/ _____

18. *ow* sounding like /ow/ _____

19. *oo* sounding like /oo/ _____

20. *oo* sounding like /ōo/ _____

21. *u* sounding like /ū/ _____

22. *u* sounding like /ōo/ _____

Phonics • *Skills Practice 2*

Synonyms and Antonyms

Focus
- Synonyms are words that are similar in meaning. *Happy* and *glad* are synonyms.
- Antonyms are words that are opposite in meaning. *Up* and *down* are antonyms.

Practice In each box, circle the *synonym* and draw a line under the *antonym* for each word shown.

1. near

close	apart	far

2. winner

helper	loser	champion

3. sick

fell	healthy	ill

Apply Write the synonym or antonym for the word in parentheses that will complete the sentence.

4. (early) If we do not hurry, we will be _____ for the movie.

5. (bend) There is a _____ in the road up ahead.

6. (float) The rock will _____ when it is thrown in the water.

Compound Words and Contractions

Practice **Underline the compound words, and circle the contractions in each sentence.**

1. Didn't you catch a grasshopper in the yard?

2. Aunt Jenny can't go to the baseball game.

3. Where's the toothbrush my dentist gave me?

4. You'll look so nice in the new cheerleader uniform.

Apply **Write the two words that make each contraction you circled. Write the two words that make each compound word you underlined.**

Contractions	Compound Words
5. _____ _____	9. _____ _____
6. _____ _____	10. _____ _____
7. _____ _____	11. _____ _____
8. _____ _____	12. _____ _____

Selection Vocabulary

Focus

special (spesh' əl) *adj.* Different from the others in some way. (page 305)

explorer (ek splôr' ûr) *n.* A person who travels to a place that is not known about. (page 308)

orchid (ôr' kid) *n.* A tropical plant with flowers that grow in many shapes and colors. (page 304)

rows (rōs) *n.* Plural of **row:** a series of people or things arranged in a line. (page 306)

chores (chôrz) *n.* Plural of **chore:** a small job around the house. (page 310)

language (lang' gwij) *n.* The speech of a country or group. (page 305)

discovered (dis kəv' ûrd) *v.* Past tense of **discover:** to be the first to find, learn of, or observe. (page 308)

sesame (se' sə mē) *n.* A tropical Asian plant bearing small, flat seeds used as food and as a source of oil. (page 308)

popular (pop' yə lər) *adj.* Liked by many people. (page 310)

wiser (wī' zûr) *adj.* Smarter. (page 311)

Draw a line matching each word on the left to its correct definition on the right.

1. explorer   **a.** to have been the first to find, learn of, or observe

2. rows   **b.** smarter

3. wiser   **c.** liked by many people

4. discovered   **d.** a series of people or things arranged in lines

5. chores   **e.** different from the others in some way

6. special   **f.** a tropical plant with flowers that grow in many shapes and colors

7. orchid   **g.** the speech of a country or group

8. popular   **h.** a tropical Asian plant bearing small, flat seeds used as food and as a source of oil

9. sesame   **i.** small jobs around the house

10. language   **j.** a person who travels to a place that is not known about

Name _____ Date _____

orchid	explorer	chores	wiser	rows
sesame	discovered	popular	special	language

11. My family shares the _____ in our house.

12. The song on the radio is very _____.

13. I saw an _____ in bloom.

14. My sister knows how to speak a different

_____.

15. Joshua _____ the present hidden in the closet.

16. The _____ in the theater were filled with people.

17. She will be _____ when she is older.

18. This is my grandmother's _____ recipe.

19. A _____ plant has many uses.

20. The _____ used a boat for his trip.

Apply Write five sentences using vocabulary words. Then write one sentence using at least two vocabulary words. Underline the words you use.

21. _____

_____

22. _____

_____

23. _____

_____

_____

24. _____

_____

25. _____

_____

26. _____

_____

Name _____ Date _____

Fact and Opinion

Focus
- A **fact** is something that can be proven true.
- An **opinion** is what someone thinks or feels. An opinion cannot be proven true.

Practice Look back at "April and Her Family." Copy two facts and two opinions.

Facts

1. _____

_____

2. _____

_____

Opinions

3. _____

_____

4. _____

_____

Read the paragraph. Draw a line under each sentence that tells a fact. Circle each sentence that gives an opinion.

The Statue of Liberty stands in New York Harbor. It was a gift to the United States from France. "Liberty Enlightening the World" is the official name of the statue. Everyone would like to see this famous lady. She is very beautiful. Workers built the statue in France, took it apart, and sent it to America to be reassembled. Maybe they should have made the statue in America. It took twenty-one years to finally complete the statue. Many immigrants saw this famous lady when they arrived in America. It is the best landmark of the United States. The Statue of Liberty is a symbol of friendship, freedom, and democracy.

Write several sentences about a place you have visited or lived in. Make sure you include facts and opinions. After writing, draw a line under each sentence that tells a fact. Circle each sentence that gives an opinion.

_____

_____

_____

_____

_____

_____

_____

Writing a Formal Letter

Think **Audience: Who** will read your formal letter?

_____

Purpose: What is your reason for writing a formal letter?

_____

Prewriting **Use this graphic organizer to plan the body of your letter.**

1. **Heading: Start with your name and address.**	
2. **Inside Address: Add the name and address of the person to whom you are writing.**	
3. **Greeting: Start with words _To Whom It May Concern,_ or _Dear,_ and then add the person's name.**	
4. **Body: Make a request.**	
5. **Closing: End your letter with _Yours truly,_ or _Sincerely,_ and then sign your name.**	

Revising   Use this checklist to revise.

☐ Is the reason for writing your letter clear?

☐ Did you make a request?

☐ Did you include enough detail about what you want to say?

☐ Did you stay on the topic?

☐ Are there any sentences you can delete?

☐ Is your letter polite?

Editing/Proofreading   Use this checklist to correct mistakes.

☐ Is every word or special term spelled correctly?

☐ Does each sentence begin with a capital letter and end with the correct punctuation mark?

☐ Does each name begin with a capital letter?

☐ Could other words be used to give more detail?

Publishing   Use this checklist to prepare for publication.

☐ Read your formal letter one more time. Make sure all the parts of a letter are included.

☐ Write or type a neat copy of your letter.

☐ Sign your letter.

/ō/, /ow/, /o͞o/, /ū/, and /oo/

Focus

- The /ō/ and /ow/ sounds can both be spelled *ow*.
- The /o͞o/ sound sounds like the word *cool*, while the /ū/ sound sounds like the word *cute*.
- The /o͞o/ and /oo/ sounds can both be spelled *oo*.

Practice   Sort the spelling words under the correct heading.

The /ō/ sound spelled ow

1. _____

The /ow/ sound spelled ow

2. _____

The /o͞o/ sound

3. _____

4. _____

5. _____

The /ū/ sound

6. _____

7. _____

Word List

1. flow
2. flower
3. cook
4. cube
5. tool
6. took
7. nook
8. noon
9. fume
10. loom

Challenge Words

11. moonbeam
12. lookout
13. mountain
14. mowing
15. crowded

The /oo/ sound

8. _____

9. _____

10. _____

Apply **Rhyming Strategy** Find the spelling word or words that rhyme with the following words. The spelling word will have the same sound and spelling pattern as the rhyming word.

11. spoon _____

12. power _____

13. fool _____

14. grow _____

15. room _____

16. look _____ _____

Visualization Strategy Read each word below. If the word is spelled correctly, write the word *correct* on the line. If the word is misspelled, write the correctly spelled word on the line.

17. fyoom _____

18. cube _____

Review

Focus

- A **common noun** names a person, a place, a thing, or an idea.

- A **proper noun** names a certain person, place, or thing. A proper noun begins with a capital letter.

- An **action verb** tells what someone or something is doing.

- A **linking verb** connects the parts of a sentence to make it complete.

- A **helping verb** helps the main verb.

- The **subject** tells what or whom the sentence is about. The **predicate** tells what the subject is or does.

Practice Read the following nouns. Write each noun under the correct column. If it is a proper noun, make sure it begins with a capital letter.

dancer	dr. green	color	america

Common Nouns

1. _____

2. _____

Proper Nouns

3. _____

4. _____

Read each sentence below. Circle the subject. Underline the predicate. On the line next to the sentence, write any words that need to start with capital letters.

5. samantha threw the ball. _____

6. the audience cheered loudly. _____

7. judy exercises every day. _____

8. my teacher read a picture book. _____

Apply **Read each sentence. Read the description of a noun or verb written in parentheses ( ). Write a noun or verb on the line to complete the sentence.**

9. _____ (proper noun) _____
(action verb) me how to play the piano.

10. My _____ (common noun) _____
(helping verb) swimming like a fish today.

11. That _____ (common noun) _____
(linking verb) my favorite.

Write three sentences. Circle the subject, and underline the predicate. Be sure to begin each sentence with a capital letter.

12. _____

13. _____

14. _____

Silent Consonants

Focus   Silent consonants in a word are not heard when the word is read.

Practice   **Read each word, and circle the letter that is silent.**

1. hour
2. doubt
3. rhyming
4. scene
5. knit
6. wrench
7. lamb
8. island
9. scent
10. listen

11. crumb
12. school
13. adjust
14. knuckles
15. muscle
16. design
17. science
18. stretch
19. wrestle
20. autumn

21. William ate (haf, half) of the pizza.

22. I did not know the (answer, anser) to her question.

23. The (sente, scent) of grilled chicken filled the air.

24. Did you (listen, lisen) to the story?

25. Carol hit her (thum, thumb) with the hammer.

26. There is a stop (sine, sign) in front of my house.

Look at each pair of words with a silent-consonant spelling pattern. Underline the spelling pattern in each word. Write a third word with the same spelling pattern on the line.

27. knee   knot   _____

28. climb   comb   _____

29. wrong   wreck   _____

30. gnat   sign   _____

31. rhombus   rhythm   _____

32. taught   daughter   _____

Prefixes *dis-*, *un-*, *mis-*, and *mid-*

Focus

- A **prefix** is added to the beginning of a word and changes the meaning of that word.
- The prefix **dis-** means "to do the opposite of" or "not to."
- The prefix **un-** means "the opposite of" or "not."
- The prefix **mis-** means "bad," "wrong," or "incorrectly."
- The prefix **mid-** means "middle."

Practice Choose a prefix from above to add to each base word. Write the meaning of the new word.

1. _____ month   _____

2. _____ agreed   _____

3. _____ treat   _____

4. _____ planned _____

5. _____ loyal   _____

6. _____ adjust   _____

7. _____ life   _____

8. _____ zipped   _____

Choose one of the following prefixes to add to the base word in parentheses ( ) to form a new word that will complete the sentence. Write the new word on the line. Then write the meaning of the new word.

dis-	un-	mid-	mis-

9. Karl was _____ (able) to attend the party.

New Meaning: _____

10. Our seats were in the _____ (section) of the stadium.

New Meaning: _____

11. My little sister sometimes _____ (obeys) our parents.

New Meaning: _____

12. I _____ (typed) my book report on the computer.

New Meaning: _____

13. Joan _____ (wrapped) her present.

New Meaning: _____

14. Wild animals are usually _____ (trusting) of human beings.

New Meaning: _____

Selection Vocabulary

Focus

ferry (fâr' ē) *n.* A boat used to carry people, cars, and goods across a narrow body of water. (page 326)

plains (plānz) *n.* An area of flat land. (page 322)

doe (dō) *n.* A female deer.(page 324)

leather (leth' ər) *n.* Material made from the skin of an animal. (page 331)

brisk (brisk) *adj.* Quick and lively. (page 326)

shed (shed) *n.* A small building used for storing things. (page 325)

recycling (rē sī' kling) *v.* Using throwaway items for another purpose. (page 320)

fabric (fab' rik) *n.* Cloth. (page 328)

citizens (sit' i zenz) *n.* Plural of **citizen:** a person who lives in a city or town. (page 332)

adopted (ə dop' təd) *v.* Past tense of **adopt:** to take care of as your own. (page 323)

Write the vocabulary word that matches each definition.

1. cloth _____

2. took care of as your own _____

3. a female deer _____

4. using throwaway items for
another purpose _____

5. material made from the skin of an
animal _____

6. a boat used to carry people, cars,
and goods across a narrow body
of water _____

7. quick and lively _____

8. people who live in a city or town _____

9. a small building used for storing
things _____

10. an area of flat land _____

Apply Tell whether the boldfaced definition that is given for the underlined word in each sentence makes sense. Circle *Yes* or *No*.

11. The <u>citizens</u> are allowed to vote.
people who live in a city or town .... Yes   No

12. Miguel <u>adopted</u> the stray kitten.
quick and lively.. Yes   No

13. The <u>doe</u> ran across the meadow.
female deer .... Yes   No

14. My coat is made from red <u>fabric</u>.
a small building used for storing things................ Yes   No

15. Doug has <u>leather</u> shoes.
material made from the skin of an animal .... Yes   No

16. Please put the lawn mower back in the <u>shed</u>.
**boat used to carry people, cars, and goods
across a narrow body of water** .... Yes   No

17. We took a <u>brisk</u> walk.
quick and lively.. Yes   No

18. Our class is learning about <u>recycling</u>.
cloth .... Yes   No

19. Our ancestors crossed the <u>plains</u> in a covered wagon.
small building used for storing things .... Yes   No

20. I took a ride on the <u>ferry</u>.
**boat used to carry people, cars, and
goods across a narrow body of water** .... Yes   No

Apply Read the following paragraph, and decide whether the underlined vocabulary words make sense as they are used. If a word does not make sense, cross it out and write the correct vocabulary word above it.

In "New Hope" by Henri Sorensen, Jimmy once again hears the story of how the town of New Hope was started. Jimmy's ancestors traveled from Denmark and then crossed the wide <u>plains</u> of America. When one of the axles on their wagon broke, the family decided to stop and make a home. They built a house for themselves and a <u>ferry</u> for the horses. Lars and Peter built a <u>shed</u> to help people cross the river. Their business was <u>brisk</u>. Soon many other people began to make homes near the river. A blacksmith built a forge, and Lars opened the New Hope General Store. The store sold <u>doe</u> for clothing and many other items.

The town grew quickly with many <u>citizens</u>. Soon the town had a tannery that made <u>recycling</u> gloves and boots. Today New Hope is still a busy, bustling town. This is all thanks to Jimmy's ancestors and their broken axle.

Name _____ Date _____

Cause and Effect

- A **cause** is *why* something happens.
- An **effect** is *what* happens.

Practice **Read each following cause, and write an effect to complete the sentence.**

1. Because we are friends, _____

_____

2. Because Joe was late, _____

_____

3. When it is the first day of school, _____

_____

4. On a cold day, _____

_____

5. I hurt my foot last week, _____

_____

6. **Effect**: Lars sailed with his family to America from Denmark.

   Cause: _____

   _____

7. **Effect**: Lars bought a wagon, two horses, a hunting rifle, tools, a tent, several bags of seeds, and plenty of food in Minnesota.

   Cause: _____

   _____

8. **Effect**: Peter and Mathilde adopted a dog.

   Cause: _____

   _____

9. **Effect**: Franz had a busy ferry business.

   Cause: _____

   _____

10. **Effect**: New Hope became a town.

    Cause: _____

    _____

Inquiry

Create a list of "ordinary" and "extraordinary" people.
Write one or two questions you would like to ask
each person.

"Ordinary" People

1. Name: _____

    a. Question: _____

    _____

    b. Question: _____

    _____

2. Name: _____

    a. Question: _____

    _____

    b. Question: _____

    _____

3. Name: _____

    Question: _____

    _____

"Extraordinary" People

4. Name: _____

    a. Question: _____

    _____

    b. Question: _____

    _____

5. Name: _____

    a. Question: _____

    _____

    b. Question: _____

    _____

6. Name: _____

    a. Question: _____

    _____

    b. Question: _____

    _____

Responding to Literature

Think   **Audience: Who** will read your response to literature?

_____

Purpose: What is your reason for writing a response to literature?

_____

Prewriting   **Use the graphic organizer below to plan your response to literature. Fill in the boxes with details about the characters.**

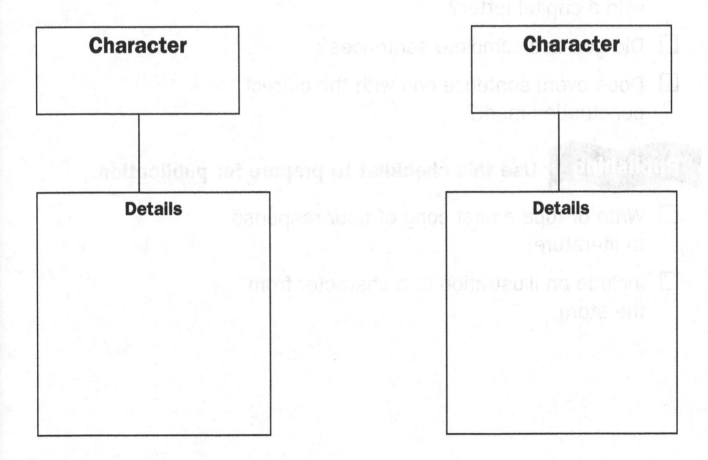

Character	Character
Details	Details

Revising
Use this checklist to revise.

☐ Did you answer the questions posed by your teacher?

☐ Does every sentence support your topic?

☐ Were any details left out that need to be added?

☐ Are your sentences in the correct order?

Editing/Proofreading
Use this checklist to correct mistakes.

☐ Is every word spelled correctly?

☐ Does every sentence and proper noun begin with a capital letter?

☐ Did you use complete sentences?

☐ Does every sentence end with the correct punctuation mark?

Publishing
Use this checklist to prepare for publication.

☐ Write or type a neat copy of your response to literature.

☐ Include an illustration of a character from the story.

Silent Consonants

Focus
Silent consonants are consonants in a word that are not heard when the word is pronounced.

Examples:
thum<u>b</u>   shou<u>l</u>d

Practice Sort the spelling words under the correct heading.

Word List
1. listen
2. castle
3. rustle
4. whistle
5. rhino
6. answer
7. doubt
8. island
9. would
10. could

Challenge Words
11. chaos
12. scenic
13. rhyme
14. hour
15. rhythm

Silent _t_

1. _____

2. _____

3. _____

4. _____

Silent _h_

5. _____

Silent _w_

6. _____

Silent _b_

7. _____

Silent _s_

8. _____

Silent _l_

9. _____

10. _____

Silent Letters

Apply **Visualization Strategy Read each word below. If the word is spelled correctly, write *correct* on the line. If the word is misspelled, write the correctly spelled word on the line.**

11. wislle _____

12. island _____

13. could _____

14. rino _____

15. rustle _____

16. dowt _____

17. casul _____

18. listen _____

19. ancer _____

20. would _____

Using an Encyclopedia

One of the most helpful resources you can use when doing an investigation is an encyclopedia. **Encyclopedias** are a set of books with information on many topics, arranged in alphabetical order. Each encyclopedia in the set is called a **volume**.

Here is an illustration of a set of encyclopedias. It has twenty volumes. Count the volumes.

Use the illustration above to answer the questions below. Write the volume letter or letters where you might find information about the following subjects. Remember that information about a person is arranged by the first letter of the person's last name.

1. Information about Denmark _____

2. Information about the history of blacksmithing _____

3. An entry on Laura Ingalls Wilder _____

4. Information about New York _____

5. An entry on Henri Sorensen _____

6. Information about ferries _____

7. Information about horses _____

Below are questions that can be answered by looking in an encyclopedia. For each question, write one or more entries, or subjects, under which you would look to find the information. For example, to answer the question, "What is the difference between a dog and a wolf?" you might look under the word *dog, wolf,* or *animals.*

8. What kind of animal is a kangaroo? _____

_____

9. What is the difference between a parrot and

a parakeet? _____

_____

10. Which city has more people living in it, New York City

or Los Angeles? _____

_____

Review

- A **complete sentence** has a subject and a predicate. In an incomplete sentence, the subject or predicate is missing.

- A **declarative** sentence makes a statement and ends in a **period** (.). An **interrogative** sentence asks a question and ends in a **question mark** (?). An **imperative** sentence gives direction and ends in a **period** (.). An **exclamatory** sentence shows strong feeling and ends in an **exclamation point** (!).

- The first letter of a proper noun, a title, or initial is **capitalized**.

- An **adjective** is a word that describes a noun. It tells how much, how many, or what kind.

- A **singular noun** names one of something. A **plural noun** names more than one.

Practice In the paragraph below, triple-underline the letters that should be capitalized. Add correct end marks, and identify each type of sentence by writing *D* (declarative), *IN* (interrogative), *IM* (imperative), or *E* (exclamatory) above the sentence. Finally, circle the adjectives.

dr. Allen Gardener came to this country from ireland many years

ago This smart man was my great-grandfather His younger brother

e. i. Gardener and his family came on the journey too I am glad my

family came to america Have you researched your ancestors You

should research that topic Learning about your ancestors is exciting

Apply In the paragraph below, triple-underline the letters that should be capitalized and add correct end marks. Look for any incomplete sentences.

Do you know where your ancestors came from Your ancestors are the members of your family who lived before you Most people have ancestors who came to america from another country Is your family from one country or many countries Freedom, money, and safety are examples of reasons people come to this country Would you be afraid to move to a distant country Our ancestors were very brave people I learning about my ancestors.

Choose three plural nouns from the paragraph above, and write the singular version of each one on the lines below. Then correct the incomplete sentence from above.

Plural Nouns	Singular Nouns

Corrected Sentence

Three-Letter Initial Consonant Blends

Focus | The sounds of *str, scr, spl,* and *spr* often combine at the beginnings of words. We say the three sounds quickly without any space between them.

Practice Add the consonant blends to the given letters to create words. Write each word on the line, and then read the word aloud.

1. *str* + and _____

2. *scr* + ape _____

3. *spl* + at _____

4. *spr* + out _____

5. *str* + ain _____

6. *scr* + eam _____

7. *spl* + otch _____

8. *spr* + ead _____

Change the beginning consonant blend of two words above to make new words. Write the word from the list and the new word.

9. _____ _____

10. _____ _____

Choose one of the consonant blends in the box to complete each word. Write the blend on the line in front of the given letters. Then write the word on the line.

str	scr	spl	spr

11. _____ inkled   _____

12. _____ ash   _____

13. _____ een   _____

14. _____ ipe   _____

15. _____ urge   _____

16. _____ awberry   _____

17. _____ int   _____

18. _____ ub   _____

Write a sentence using a word with the consonant blend written in parentheses ( ).

19. (str) _____

20. (scr) _____

21. (spl) _____

22. (spr) _____

Inflectional Endings and Comparative Ending *-er*

Focus

- The **inflectional endings** *-ing* and *-ed* can be added to a base word. The meaning of the word is not changed, only the form and function. The *-ing* ending lets you know something is happening now. The *-ed* ending is used when something has already happened.

- The **comparative ending** *-er* shows a comparison between two things. The ending *-er* is usually added to a base word.

Practice Write each base word under the correct ending. Write the word, and add the correct suffix. Use the same base word with both inflectional endings. Remember that the *-er* ending should be used to make a *comparison*.

young	fail	glow	cheap
moist	earn	high	pick

Inflectional Endings   **Comparative Ending**

    -ing   *-ed*   *-er*

1. _____   _____   5. _____

2. _____   _____   6. _____

3. _____   _____   7. _____

4. _____   _____   8. _____

Suffixes -er and -ness

 Focus
- The suffix -er means "one who."
- The suffix -ness means "state of being."

Practice **Add the suffix to the base word, and write the new word. Then write the meaning of the new word.**

1. surf   + er   = _____

New Meaning: _____

2. blind + ness = _____

New Meaning: _____

Apply **Choose one of the words below, and add -er or -ness. Write the word on the line.**

train	happy	work	fond	loud

3. The tiger _____ shouted his commands.

4. Carol has a _____ for puppies.

5. Sally was filled with _____ after she won the award.

6. Jeff's office needs to hire one more part-time

_____.

Selection Vocabulary

Focus **demanding** (di mand' ing) *v.* Asking for forcefully. (page 342)

allowed (ə loud') *v.* Past tense of **allow:** to let someone do something. (page 347)

fair (fâr) *adj.* Not favoring one more than another. (page 342)

laws (lôz) *n.* Plural of **law:** a rule made by a government. (page 342)

graduated (graj' o͞o ā' təd) *v.* Past tense of **graduate:** to finish school. (page 349)

college (kol' ij) *n.* A school that offers education beyond the high school level. (page 349)

arrested (ə res' təd) *v.* Past tense of **arrest:** to hold by authority of the law. (page 350)

prejudice (prej' ə dis) *n.* Unfair treatment of a group of people. (page 357)

content (kon' tent) *n.* What is in something. (page 354)

section (sek' shən) *n.* A part. (page 350)

Complete each sentence by filling in the blank with a vocabulary word from this lesson.

1. Martin Luther King Jr. _____ from high school two years early.

2. He then attended _____.

3. There was once a "White Only" _____ on public buses.

4. People were _____ to sit in only certain sections of the buses.

5. Some _____ kept African Americans out of many schools and jobs.

6. Martin Luther King Jr. did not think these laws were

   _____.

7. Rosa Parks was _____ for not giving a white man her seat on the bus.

8. People led protests _____ fair laws for all people.

9. Martin Luther King Jr. wanted to end _____.

10. In a famous speech, Martin Luther King Jr. said that people

    should be judged by the "_____ of their character."

Apply **Complete the following activities.**

11. What is the base word of **_allowed?_** _____

List two other words with the same base.

_____   _____

12. Which one of the vocabulary words is a multiple-meaning

word? _____

13. What is the base word of **_graduated?_**_____

List two other words with the same base.

_____   _____

14. List a synonym for **_laws._** _____

15. List an antonym for **_arrested._** _____

16. Define **_college_** in your own words.

_____

_____

17. What is the base word of **_demanding?_**

_____

List another word with the same base._____

18. Write about a time you were not treated in a *fair* way.

_____

_____

19. How did some *laws* affect African Americans?

_____

_____

20. Explain how the Montgomery Public Buses once showed *prejudice* toward certain people.

_____

_____

21. Why was Rosa Parks *arrested?*

_____

_____

22. What do you think Martin Luther King Jr. meant when he said "the *content* of their character"?

_____

_____

Writing a Persuasive Paragraph

Think **Audience: Who** will read your persuasive paragraph?

_____

Purpose: What is your reason for writing a persuasive paragraph?

_____

Prewriting Use this graphic organizer to plan your paragraph. Write your topic in the middle square. Write reasons that support your topic in the smaller squares.

Reason	Reason

Topic Sentence

Reason	Reason

Revising Use this checklist to revise.

☐ Do you persuade others to think a certain way?

☐ Do you have good reasons that support your opinion?

☐ Are there facts or details that need to be added?

Editing/Proofreading Use this checklist to correct mistakes.

☐ Is your paragraph indented?

☐ Is every word or special term spelled correctly?

☐ Does every sentence start with a capital letter?

☐ Does every sentence end with the correct punctuation mark?

Publishing Use this checklist to prepare for publication.

☐ Write or type a neat copy of your persuasive paragraph.

☐ Read your paragraph one more time. Make sure all the parts are there.

Three-Letter Initial Consonant Blends

Focus
- A consonant blend is two or more consonants together in a word, and each sound can be heard.
- Some common three-letter consonant blends are *str*, *scr*, *spr*, and *spl*.

Word List
1. straw
2. split
3. scrape
4. stretch
5. splash
6. scream
7. sprawl
8. sprout
9. strange
10. scratch

Challenge Words
11. strength
12. spry
13. screen
14. sprinkle
15. splurge

Practice   Sort the spelling words under the correct heading.

str blend

1. _____

2. _____

3. _____

scr blend

4. _____

5. _____

6. _____

spr blend

7. _____

8. _____

spl blend

9. _____

10. _____

Visualization Strategy Circle the correct spelling for each word. Then write the correct word on the line.

11. skrach   scratch   _____

12. strange   stiranj   _____

13. sprout   spurowt   _____

14. spullit   split   _____

15. scream   skreem   _____

Meaning Strategy Write the spelling word that best completes each sentence.

16. The dolphins made a big _____ at the end of their show.

17. We had to _____ the old paint off the dresser before we could put on a new coat.

18. There were so many new buildings being built in the city that

it began to _____ out to the countryside.

19. Could I please have a _____ for my drink?

20. The balloon began to _____ as it filled with air.

Using Multiple Sources

Write your investigation question and your conjecture.

_____

_____

_____

_____

There are many different sources you can use for your investigation. Complete the questions about two possible sources you could use.

First Source: _____

- What type of information does this source contain?

_____

- What might you learn from this source about your question?

_____

_____

_____

- Find the name of one source of this kind (in a library) that you might be able to use in your investigation.

_____

_____

Second Source: _____

_____

- What type of information does this source contain?

_____

_____

- What might you learn from this source?

_____

_____

- Find the name of one source of this kind (in a library) that you might be able to use in your investigation.

_____

_____

Review

- An **adjective** describes a noun or a pronoun. You can use a **comparative adjective** to compare nouns or pronouns.

- An **article** is a special kind of adjective. The three articles are *a, an,* and *the.*

- **Capitalize** the days of the week and the months of the year. You must also capitalize the names of cities and states.

- A **comma** is used after each item in a series or list of things, except after the last one.

- A sentence must have **subject and verb agreement.** This means the subject and the verb must both be singular or they must both be plural.

- An **adverb** is a word that describes a verb by telling how, where, or when.

Practice   **In the paragraph below, triple-underline letters that should be capitalized. Insert commas between items in a series, and circle the comparative adjectives.**

Did you know China has the world's largest population? India is the next biggest   then the United States   and then Indonesia. The three most populated states in the United States are california, texas and new york. texas is the largest in size of the three states, and california is bigger than new york. Of the cities in these states, New York City has the biggest population. Next is Los Angeles, which is in california.

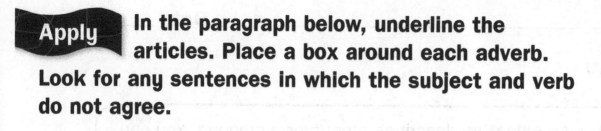

In the paragraph below, underline the articles. Place a box around each adverb. Look for any sentences in which the subject and verb do not agree.

In October my family traveled to China to see where our ancestors came from. We left the United States on a Monday and arrived in China on Wednesday. The airplane ride felt like the longest three days of my life. We had packed enough shirts, shorts, and shoes for five weeks. I had packed my suitcase rapidly because I had waited so long. My sister's suitcase were smaller than mine, but I quickly carried mine through the airport. We did not leave China until November. What a great trip!

In the paragraph above, find the sentence in which the subject and verb do not agree. Rewrite the sentence correctly on the lines below.

_____

_____

/ow/ and /aw/

> **Focus**
> - The /ow/ sound can be spelled *ow* and *ou_*.
> - The /aw/ sound can be spelled *aw* and *au_*.

Practice Underline the /ow/ or /aw/ spelling pattern in each word. Write a rhyming word that has the same spelling pattern. Underline the /ow/ or /aw/ spelling pattern in the rhyming word.

1. frown _____

2. Paul _____

3. sound _____

4. claw _____

5. now _____

6. lawn _____

Read the clue, and fill in the correct /ow/ or /aw/ spelling pattern to complete the word.

7. a place to live   h_____se

8. circus performer   cl_____n

9. to move on your knees   cr_____l

10. a summer month   _____gust

11. a large hill   m_____ntain

12. a rule   l_____

Apply Circle the correct word that completes the sentence.

13. Missy looked for shapes in the _____.

    a. clowds   **b.** clouds   **c.** clauds   **d.** cloweds

14. A kite was _____ in the tree's highest branches.

    a. caught   **b.** cowt   **c.** cawt   **d.** caut

15. The daisy is my aunt's favorite _____.

    a. flouer   **b.** flauer   **c.** flower   **d.** floer

16. My dog hurt his _____.

    a. paw   **b.** pau   **c.** pou   **d.** pah

17. There was a long line at the water _____.

    a. fauntain   **b.** fountain   **c.** fowtain   **d.** fowten

18. The rocket was almost ready to _____.

    a. launch   **b.** lownch   **c.** lounch   **d.** lawntch

19. I heard a coyote _____.

    a. hawl   **b.** houl   **c.** holl   **d.** howl

20. What made that _____ noise?

    a. lowd   **b.** loud   **c.** lawd   **d.** laud

Suffixes -y, -ful, -less, and -ly

Focus
- A **suffix** is added to the end of a base word. Adding a suffix changes the meaning of the word.
- The suffix **-ly** means "in a certain way."
- The suffix **-y** means "full of."
- The suffix **-less** means "without."
- The suffix **-ful** means "full of."

Practice Choose a suffix from above to add to each base word. Write the meaning of the new word.

1. flaw_____ _____

2. thirst_____ _____

3. fond_____ _____

4. youth_____ _____

Write two sentences using two of the words from above.

5. -ly _____

6. -y _____

Apply Choose one of the following suffixes to add to the base word in parentheses ( ) to form a new word that will complete the sentence. Write the new word on the line. Then write the meaning of the new word.

-ly	-y	-less	-ful

7. Do not be _____ (care) when carrying the glass vase.

New Meaning: _____

8. I get scared when it is _____ (storm) outside.

New Meaning: _____

9. Spread the peanut butter _____ (even) on the bread.

New Meaning: _____

10. My dad's new car is very _____ (power).

New Meaning: _____

11. The autumn air is sometimes _____ (chill).

New Meaning: _____

12. Wendy _____ (sudden) dropped her book.

New Meaning: _____

Selection Vocabulary

Focus

calves (kavz) *n.* Plural of **calf:** the back part of the lower leg. (page 374)

ached (ākt) *v.* Past tense of **ache:** to hurt with a dull, steady pain. (page 388)

pounding (poun' ding) *v.* Beating. (page 382)

pale (pāl) *adj.* Light in color. (page 382)

glimpse (glimps) *n.* A quick look. (page 378)

daydreamed (dā' drēmd) *v.* Past tense of **daydream:** to have a happy thought about things a person would like to do or have happen. (page 367)

shuffled (shuf' əld) *v.* Past tense of **shuffle:** to drag the feet while walking. (page 382)

slipped (slipt) *v.* Past tense of **slip:** to put on. (page 382)

strolled (strōld) *v.* Past tense of **stroll:** to walk in a slow, relaxed way. (page 378)

shucked (shukt) *v.* Past tense of **shuck:** to take off. (page 382)

1. pounding _____

_____

2. shuffled _____

_____

3. pale _____

_____

4. ached _____

_____

5. shucked _____

_____

6. calves _____

_____

7. daydreamed _____

_____

8. strolled _____

_____

9. glimpse _____

_____

10. slipped _____

_____

Apply With a partner, take turns performing each of the vocabulary words below. You do not have to go in order. Put a check mark (✔) by the words your partner was able to determine correctly. Put an X by the words he or she could not determine.

calves	ached	pounding	pale	glimpse
daydreamed	shuffled	slipped	strolled	shucked

Answer the following questions.

Which word was the easiest to perform? _____

Why? _____

Which word was the most difficult to perform? _____

Why? _____

Which word was the easiest to determine from your

partner's actions? _____

Which word was the most difficult to determine from your

partner's actions? _____

Write a story using all the vocabulary words. Underline the vocabulary words in your story.

_____

_____

_____

_____

_____

_____

_____

_____

_____

_____

_____

_____

_____

_____

_____

_____

_____

_____

Describing an Accomplishment

Think Audience: **Who** will read your description?

_____

Purpose: What is your reason for writing a description?

_____

Prewriting Use the web below to plan your description. Write the event you are describing in the center box. Then write descriptive details in the outer boxes.

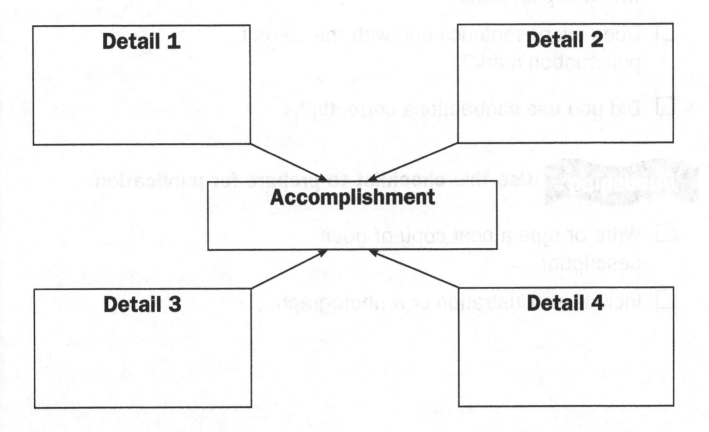

Detail 1	Detail 2

Accomplishment

Detail 3	Detail 4

Revising — Use this checklist to revise.

- ☐ Does every sentence support your topic?
- ☐ Did you use descriptive details?
- ☐ Were any details left out that need to be added?
- ☐ Are the events written in the correct order?

Editing/ Proofreading — Use this checklist to correct mistakes.

- ☐ Are the paragraphs indented?
- ☐ Is every word spelled correctly?
- ☐ Does every sentence and proper noun begin with a capital letter?
- ☐ Does every sentence end with the correct punctuation mark?
- ☐ Did you use contractions correctly?

Publishing — Use this checklist to prepare for publication.

- ☐ Write or type a neat copy of your description.
- ☐ Include an illustration or a photograph.

/ow/ and /aw/

Focus
- The /aw/ sound sounds like the word *lawn*.
- Two ways the /aw/ sound can be spelled are *aw* and *au_*.
- The /ow/ sound sounds like the word *brown*.
- It can be spelled *ow* and *ou_*.

Practice **Sort the spelling words under the correct heading.**

/aw/ spelled aw

1. _____

2. _____

3. _____

4. _____

/aw/ spelled au_

5. _____

/aw/ spelled ow

6. _____

7. _____

8. _____

9. _____

/aw/ spelled ou_

10. _____

Word List
1. tawny
2. tower
3. pause
4. pounding
5. shawl
6. shower
7. claw
8. clown
9. awe
10. owl

Challenge Words
11. applaud
12. awkward
13. August
14. warehouse
15. fountain

Rhyming Strategy Write the spelling word or words that rhyme with each pair of words below.

11. power   flower   _____   _____

12. draw   saw   _____

13. down   town   _____

14. brawny   scrawny   _____

15. fowl   growl   _____

16. crawl   sprawl   _____

Meaning Strategy Fill in the blank with the spelling word that best completes the sentence. One word will be used twice in the same sentence.

pause	owl	pounding	awe

17. The sound of a _____ hammer sometimes

gives me a _____ headache.

18. Television shows have to _____ for commercials.

19. I was in _____ of the height of the Washington Monument.

20. An _____ usually hunts at night.

Using Newspapers and Magazines

Find a story or an article in a newspaper or a magazine that is related to your unit investigation. Then answer the questions below.

1. Is your article from a newspaper or a magazine?

_____

_____

2. What is the name and date of the newspaper or magazine?

_____

_____

3. What is the name of the article?

_____

_____

4. What is the article about?

_____

_____

_____

_____

_____

5. How does the article help you with your unit investigation?

_____

_____

_____

_____

_____

Review

- A **colon** is used to introduce a list and to separate the hour and the minutes when writing the time.

- A **pronoun** is a word that takes the place of a noun in a sentence. A singular noun must be replaced with a singular pronoun. A plural noun must be replaced with a plural pronoun. Every pronoun must match the gender of the noun it replaces.

- A **contraction** combines two words. A contraction may be formed by combining a verb and the word *not* or by combining a pronoun and a verb.

- A **possessive noun** ends in an apostrophe s ('s). A plural possessive noun ends in just an apostrophe (').

- Three **verb tenses** are present, past, and future.

Practice For the paragraph below, put colons in the correct places. Circle the pronouns, and underline the possessive nouns.

My family went to a powwow this weekend. It was an interesting event. We all had a great time. My favorite part of the powwow was the 2 30 dance performance. My brother's favorite part was the fry bread. He said he could have eaten it all day. When we go next year, we will take my mom's camera. I want to have pictures to remember the trip to the powwow.

Apply For the paragraph below, place a circle around the contractions. Look for examples of sentences that use present-, past-, and future-tense verbs.

Our class will go on a field trip today. We'll go to the historical center. It's one of my favorite places to go. It's one of my sister's favorite places too. We went there when we were five years old. It was really fun. This trip will be a lot of fun too. Our bus will leave at 8:15 in the morning. It will return to the school at 2:20 P.M. It'll be a fun day.

Find an example of a sentence using each type of verb tense in the paragraph above. Write each sentence on the lines below.

Present: _____

_____

Past: _____

_____

Future: _____

_____

Unit Review

- The *ow* spelling pattern can make the /ō/ and /ow/ sounds.
- The *u, u_e, _ue,* and *_ew* spelling patterns can make the /ū/ and /o͞o/ sounds.
- The *oo* spelling pattern can make the /o͞o/ and /oo/ sounds.
- The *ow* and *ou_* spelling patterns can make the /ow/ sound.
- The *aw* and *au_* spelling patterns can make the /aw/ sound.

Practice Circle the spelling pattern in each word below. Write the sound each word makes: /aw/, /ow/, /oo/, /o͞o/,/ō/, or /ū/.

1. straw _____

2. burrow _____

3. hook _____

4. few _____

5. snow _____

6. boost _____

7. counting _____

8. screw _____

9. laundry _____

10. power _____

Silent Consonants and Three-Letter Initial Consonant Blends

- Silent consonants in a word are not heard when the word is read.
- The sounds of str, scr, spl, and spr often combine at the beginning of words. We say the three sounds quickly without any space between them.

Practice Read each word below. Circle a consonant blend or silent consonant that is in each word. Identify the spelling pattern circled by writing *blend* or *silent consonant* on the line.

1. tomb _____

3. scramble _____

2. stroke _____

4. writer _____

Apply Use one of the following words to fill in each blank.

strawberries	spray
knot	stripes

5. Hannah had a _____ in her shoelace.

6. Be sure to put on bug _____ before camping.

7. The American flag has red and white _____.

8. _____ are my favorite fruit.

Multiple-Meaning Words

Focus Multiple-meaning words are words that are spelled and pronounced the same but have different meanings.

Practice Circle the word in each pair that has multiple meanings.

1. watch   girl   4. food   found

2. door   sink   5. paper   ball

3. bill   tree   6. desk   cast

Apply Choose two of the multiple-meaning words from above. Write different sentences using the different meanings for the words.

7. _____

8. _____

_____

9. _____

10. _____

Words with the Same Base

Focus A base word can give a clue to the meaning of other words in the word family.

Practice Write the base word for each word family.

1. stars, starfish, starlight _____

2. handmade, handbook, handsaw _____

3. classroom, bedroom, bathroom _____

4. untrustworthy, trusting, trustful _____

Apply Fill in the blank with a word that has the same base.

5. airfield, airport, _____

6. correction, correctly, _____

7. blur, blurry, _____

8. completely, completed, _____

9. washing, washed, _____

10. teach, teaching, _____

11. writer, written, _____

12. naturally, unnatural, _____

Selection Vocabulary

 Focus   **treated** (trēt' əd) *v.* Past tense of **treat:** to behave toward or deal with in a certain way. (page 401)

support (sə pôrt') *v.* To provide for. (page 411)

border (bôr' dər) *n.* The line where one country ends and another begins. (page 402)

community (kə mū' ni tē) *n.* People who live together in the same town or place. (page 414)

weakened (wē' kənd) *v.* Past tense of **weaken:** to grow less strong. (page 414)

strike (strīk) *v.* To stop work in order to get better pay and working conditions. (page 412)

union (ūn' yən) *n.* A group of workers who join together to get better pay and working conditions. (page 401)

boycott (boi' kot) *v.* To refuse to buy something until workers are treated better. (page 412)

crops (krops) *n.* Plural of **crop:** fruits, vegetables, or other plants that are grown on a farm and sold. (page 409)

awarded (ə wôr' dəd) *v.* Past tense of **award:** to give honor after careful thought. (page 417)

Complete each sentence with a vocabulary word.

1. In the 1880s Cesario Chavez crossed the

   _____ into Texas.

2. Librado Chavez, Cesario's son, worked hard to

   _____ his family.

3. Cesar Chavez believed workers should be

   _____ fairly.

4. He helped farmworkers come together to form

   a _____.

5. During the Great Depression, the family worked by

   picking _____.

6. In 1965 Chavez asked grape pickers to _____.

7. Chavez wanted people to _____ grapes.

8. Going on hunger strikes must have

   _____ Chavez.

9. Cesar Chavez was _____ the Medal of
   Freedom.

10. He is known throughout the Mexican American

    _____.

Apply Use each vocabulary word in a sentence.

11. _____

12. _____

13. _____

14. _____

15. _____

16. _____

_____

17. _____

_____

18. _____

_____

19. _____

_____

20. _____

List antonyms for the vocabulary words listed below.

Vocabulary Words	Antonyms
21. support	_____
22. weakened	_____
23. boycott	_____
24. awarded	_____
25. strike	_____

List synonyms for the vocabulary words listed below.

Vocabulary Words	Synonyms
26. support	_____
27. awarded	_____
28. community	_____

Drawing Conclusions

Focus Readers can draw conclusions about a character or an event in a story by using information in the story's words and pictures.

Practice **Read the following paragraph. Then answer the questions below by drawing conclusions.**

Our teacher, Ms. Smith, began talking to herself. "Now where are they? I cannot read without them." She looked through her desk drawers. She looked in her purse. She patted her pockets. As Ms. Smith scratched her head, we began to giggle. She found what she had been looking for. "I always leave them up there," she laughed.

What was Ms. Smith doing? _____

_____

Why did the students giggle when Ms. Smith scratched her head?

_____

_____

Write one clue that lets you know Ms. Smith was looking for her glasses.

_____

_____

Read the following pages of "Cesar E. Chavez." Draw one conclusion after reading, and write it down. Write one sentence from the text that helped you draw your conclusion.

1. page 406

Conclusion: _____

Supporting Sentence: _____

_____

2. page 409

Conclusion: _____

Supporting Sentence: _____

_____

3. page 411

Conclusion: _____

_____

Supporting Sentence: _____

_____

4. page 412

Conclusion: _____

Supporting Sentence: _____

_____

Writing a Biography

Think **Audience: Who** will read your biography?

_____

Purpose: What is your reason for writing a biography?

_____

Prewriting **Use this graphic organizer to record the main idea and details of your biography.**

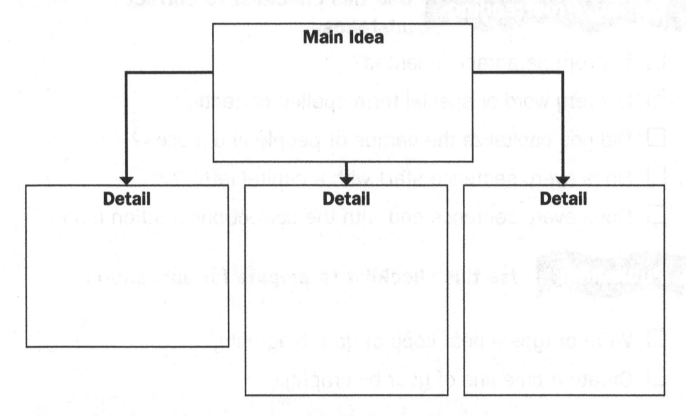

On a separate sheet of paper, write at least three
important dates and the event that occurred on
each date in the person's life.

Revising — Use this checklist to revise.

- ☐ Did you include the main idea in the first paragraph?
- ☐ Do your details support the main idea?
- ☐ Are the events in the proper sequence, and do they flow from one event to the next?
- ☐ Did you leave out any important dates or events?
- ☐ Did you use clear, specific words that tell where, when, and how things happened?

Editing/Proofreading — Use this checklist to correct mistakes.

- ☐ Is every paragraph indented?
- ☐ Is every word or special term spelled correctly?
- ☐ Did you capitalize the names of people and places?
- ☐ Does every sentence start with a capital letter?
- ☐ Does every sentence end with the correct punctuation mark?

Publishing — Use this checklist to prepare for publication.

- ☐ Write or type a neat copy of your biography.
- ☐ Create a time line of your biography.

Unit Review

Focus

- The *oo* spelling makes different sounds. One sound is /oo/, as in the word *cook*.

- Another sound is /o͞o/, as in the word *root*.

- One spelling for the /aw/ sound is *aw*, as in the word *crawl*.

- The *ow* spelling can make the sound of /ō/, as in the word *row*. It can also make the /ow/ sound, as in the word *cow*.

- Three-letter consonant blends are when three consonants are together in a word and each consonant keeps its own sound when pronounced, as in the word *straw*.

Word List
1. law
2. low
3. boot
4. book
5. doom
6. took
7. allow
8. arrow
9. string
10. spring

Challenge Words
11. describe
12. strict
13. scramble
14. downtown
15. borrow

Practice **Sort the spelling words under the correct heading.**

ow as in *flow*

1. _____

2. _____

ow as in *now*

3. _____

/oo/ sound

4. _____

5. _____

/oo/ sound

6. _____

7. _____

/aw/ sound

8. _____

Three-letter initial consonant blends

9. _____

10. _____

Apply **Rhyming Strategy** Write the spelling word or words that rhyme with each word or pair of words below.

11. cook   look   _____ _____

12. room   gloom   _____ _____

13. claw   jaw   _____ _____

14. crow   slow   _____ _____

15. bring   sing   _____ _____

Visualization Strategy Read each pair of words below. Circle the correctly spelled word. Then write the correctly spelled word on the line.

16. bute   boot   _____

17. ulou   allow   _____

18. door   dore   _____

19. arrow   airo   _____

20. stringe   string   _____

Using New Technology

After you have conducted your investigation, you could use a form of technology—such as a computer, a video camera, or a color printer—to present your information.

Complete the questions below about using a form of new technology to help present information.

- **First Idea for a Presentation**

   1. What would be one way to present your information without using new technology?

   _____

   _____

   _____

   _____

   2. How could you use a form of new technology to help you present the same information?

   _____

   _____

   _____

   _____

• **Second Idea for a Presentation**

3. What would be another way to present your information without using new technology?

_____

_____

_____

_____

4. How could you use a form of new technology to help you present the same information?

_____

_____

_____

_____

Study Skills • *Skills Practice 2*

Review

- The greeting and closing in a letter begins with a **capital letter.** A **comma** is placed after the name of the person in the salutation and after the closing.

- The **order of words** in a sentence is important. Words need to be placed in the correct order for the sentence to make sense.

- A **quotation mark** is used right before and right after the words a speaker says.

- A **comma** is used to separate a quotation from the person who said it.

- A **conjunction** is a word that connects words or ideas. *And, or,* and *but* are conjunctions.

- A **compound sentence** is made when two sentences with similar ideas are combined into one sentence.

Practice In the letter below, triple-underline the letters in the greeting and closing that need to be capitalized. Place commas and quotation marks in the correct positions.

dear Uncle Charles

Thank you for the birthday gift. I really like books and always want more to read. When I showed my sister the book you sent me, she was happy. I love that book and wanted to buy it she said. I will let her borrow it when I am finished reading it. I am excited to see you in two months when we come visit!

thank you

Daniel

In the letter below, find the sentence with the incorrect word order. Write it in the correct order on the line below. Then underline the compound sentences, and circle the conjunctions.

May 5, 2008

Dear Mr. Green,

I really like the shoes your company makes. I would like to buy a pair, but my mom said I have to save my money. When I told my dad, he said "It is good to have goals and reasons to save money." I with him agree, and I him thanked for giving me a goal. I hope I will have enough money for the shoes soon.

Sincerely,

Noah

_____

_____

Vocabulary Word Web Resources

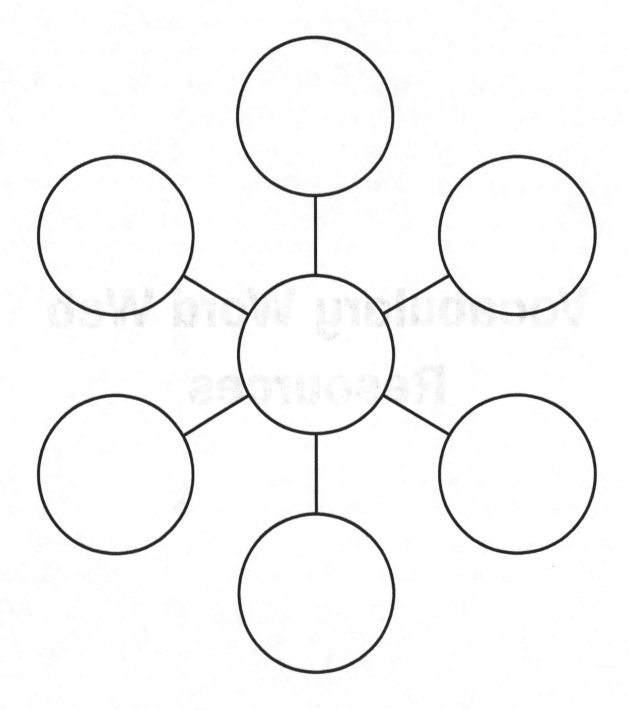

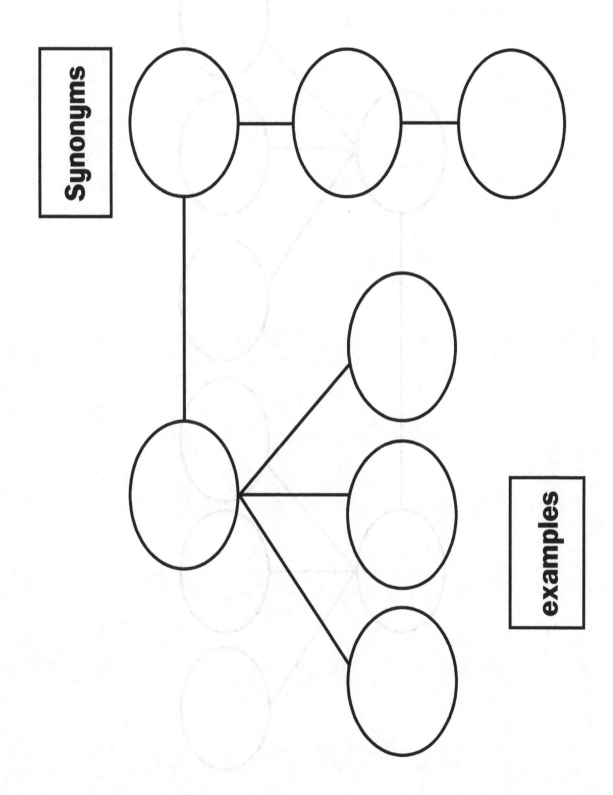

Synonyms

examples

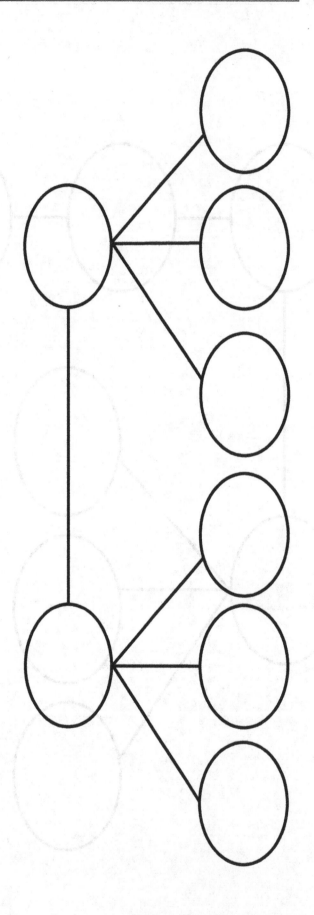

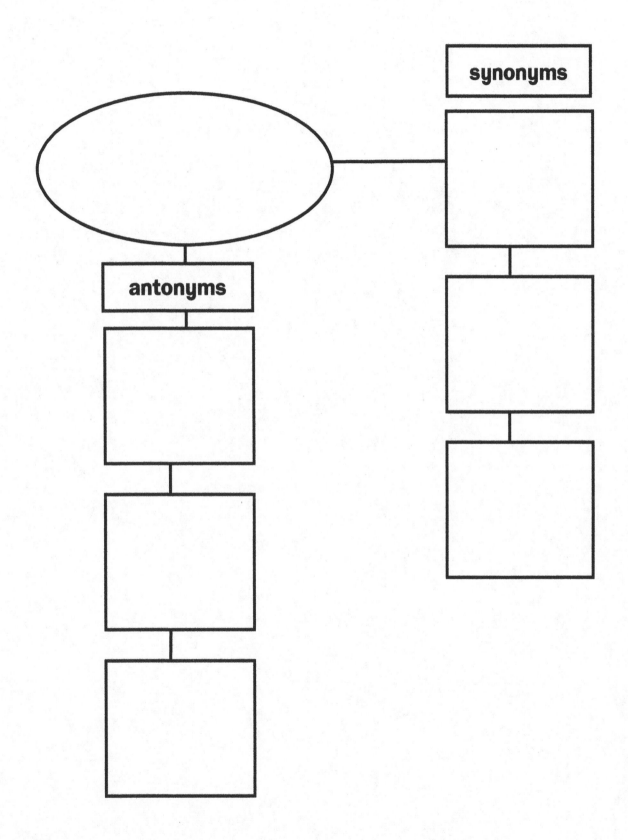

synonyms

antonyms